GRADE 3

Student Weekly Assessment

McGraw-Hill **Macmillan/McGraw-Hill**

A

The *McGraw·Hill* Companies

 Macmillan/McGraw-Hill

Published by Macmillan/McGraw-Hill, of McGraw-Hill Education, a division of The McGraw-Hill Companies, Inc.,
Two Penn Plaza, New York, New York 10121.

Printed in the United States of America

2 3 4 5 6 7 8 9 021 13 12 11 10 09

Contents

Contents

© Macmillan/McGraw-Hill

Contents

Weekly Assessment

Contents

Reading Sample

DIRECTIONS

Read "The First Day." Then read each question. Decide which is the best answer to each question. Mark the space for the answer you have chosen.

The First Day

Being "the new kid" at school is always a little scary. Kenny knew that everyone would look at him. He also figured that no one would talk to him. After all, everyone had their friends already.

Kenny walked into Mrs. Lyon's class and looked around. Everyone looked at Kenny. Some kids whispered to each other. Kenny didn't know what to do. Then a girl waved at him. She told him there was an empty desk next to her. Kenny smiled and walked over to her.

S-1 How does Kenny feel at the end of the story?

- Ⓐ Frightened
- Ⓑ Excited
- Ⓒ Angry
- Ⓓ Happy

S-2 What is this story mainly about?

- Ⓐ Having a best friend
- Ⓑ Going to a new school
- Ⓒ Being a good student
- Ⓓ Finding a desk at school

STOP

Revising and Editing Sample

DIRECTIONS

Read the introduction and the passage that follows. Then read each question and fill in the correct answer.

Jessica wrote this story about a girl named Hannah. She wants you to review her paper. As you read, think about the corrections and improvements that Jessica should make. Then answer the questions that follow.

Brand New Bag

(1) Hannah wasn't happy about starting third grade. (2) She did want to see her friends! (3) She also loved to read and write. (4) But she didn't want to use her brother Billy's old school bag.

(5) Hannah's mom thought Billy's blue bag was just like new. (6) But Hannah didn't like the color blue. (7) She wanted a purple school bag.

(8) Hannah sat at the kitchen table with a frown. (9) She poked her breakfast with a fork. (10) Then it was time for school. (11) Hannah had a surprise waiting for her. (12) New purple school bag by the door!

S-3 What change, if any, should be made in sentence 2?

  (A) Change *She* to **He**

  (B) Change *want* to **wanting**

  (C) Change the exclamation mark to a period

  (D) Make no change

S-4 What is the **BEST** way to revise sentence 12?

  (A) There were a new purple school bag by the door!

  (B) A new purple school bag by the door there was!

  (C) A new purple school bag there was by the door!

  (D) There was a new purple school bag by the door!

© Macmillan/McGraw-Hill

STOP

Grade 3

Selection Tests

Macmillan/McGraw-Hill

First Day Jitters

DIRECTIONS
Decide which is the best answer to each question.

1 Sarah wants to stay in bed because she —

   A is very tired

   B has a bad cold

   C does not want breakfast

   D is nervous about school

2 Which word best describes Mr. Hartwell?

   A Puzzled

   B Selfish

   C Caring

   D Angry

3 Which word best describes Sarah's principal?

   A Silly

   B Kind

   C Upset

   D Confused

GO ON ➡

4 What happens last in this story?

   A Sarah walks into the kitchen.

   B Sarah meets the students in her class.

   C Mr. Hartwell gives Sarah her lunchbox.

   D Mr. Hartwell drives Sarah to her new school.

5 The ending of "First Day Jitters" is surprising because —

   A Sarah is a teacher, not a student

   B Sarah is just pretending to be nervous

   C the students are happy to meet Sarah

   D Mr. Hartwell doesn't really want Sarah to go to school

6 Who is Mr. Hartwell?

   A Sarah's father

   B Sarah's teacher

   C Sarah's husband

   D Sarah's neighbor

7 Read this sentence from the story.

She <u>fumbled</u> into her clothes.

The word <u>fumbled</u> means that she was being —

- **A** graceful
- **B** fearless
- **C** clumsy
- **D** mean

8 Read this sentence from the story.

"<u>Nonsense</u>," said Mr. Hartwell.

The word <u>nonsense</u> means something that —

- **A** makes no sense
- **B** has a lot of sense
- **C** looks like sense
- **D** has sense again

9 Read this sentence.

Sarah moaned as she <u>trudged</u> into the kitchen.

The word <u>trudged</u> means that she walked in a —

- **A** strong, angry way
- **B** light, skip-hopping way
- **C** slow, heavy-footed way
- **D** fast, businesslike way

GO ON ▶

10 Which words best describe Sarah? Explain your answer and support it with details from the story.

_____

_____

_____

_____

_____

_____

STOP

Amazing Grace

DIRECTIONS
Decide which is the best answer to each question.

1 Read the chart and answer the question below.

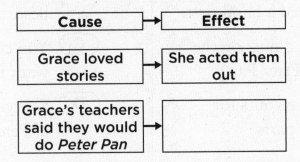

Cause	→	Effect
Grace loved stories	→	She acted them out
Grace's teachers said they would do *Peter Pan*	→	

Which of these belongs in the empty box?

(A) She sailed the seven seas.

(B) Grace played all the parts herself.

(C) She rubbed a magic lamp.

(D) Grace wanted to be Peter Pan.

2 Raj said Grace couldn't play Peter Pan because —

(A) she couldn't fly

(B) she was a girl

(C) she was too old

(D) he raised his hand first

3 Natalie said Grace couldn't play Peter Pan because —

(A) Peter Pan wasn't black

(B) Peter Pan was tiny

(C) Grace wasn't good at acting

(D) Grace couldn't learn the part

GO ON ➡

4 How did the teacher decide who should get the part of Peter Pan?

A She picked a name from a hat.

B She chose the student who raised a hand first.

C She gave a quiz on the story of Peter Pan.

D She held tryouts for different parts.

5 On Saturday, Nana took Grace to see —

A a movie

B a museum

C a ballet

D a play

6 In this story, what lesson did Nana want Grace to learn?

A Friends don't know everything.

B Grandmothers know best.

C You can be anything you want to be.

D Everyone loves the story of Peter Pan.

7 Read this sentence from the story.

Above the dancer it said STUNNING NEW JULIET.

Which meaning from a dictionary best fits the way stunning is used in this sentence?

A Very attractive

B Having dark hair

C Well paid

D Not experienced

GO ON

Selection Test

8 Read this sentence from the story.

The sign outside read *Romeo and Juliet* in <u>sparkling</u> lights.

Which word means the same as <u>sparkling</u>?

- **A** Dull
- **B** Shining
- **C** Winking
- **D** Yellow

9 Read this sentence from the story.

"You were <u>fantastic</u>!" whispered Natalie.

The word <u>fantastic</u> means —

- **A** scary
- **B** okay
- **C** awful
- **D** excellent

GO ON ▶

10 How did Grace prepare for the Peter Pan audition? Explain your answer and support it with details from the story.

_____

_____

_____

_____

_____

_____

_____

Earth Smart

DIRECTIONS
Decide which is the best answer to each question.

1 Look at the chart below.

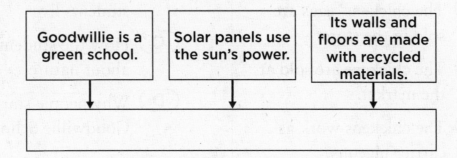

Which of these belongs in the empty box?

Ⓐ The Goodwillie School is located in Ada, Michigan.

Ⓑ The solar power heats the school in the winter.

Ⓒ The Goodwillie School is friendly to the environment.

Ⓓ The outdoor deck is made from sawdust and recycled milk jugs.

2 At the Goodwillie Environmental School, both milk jugs and sawdust are —

Ⓐ used in art projects

Ⓑ used in building the deck

Ⓒ sold in the school store

Ⓓ fed to the chickens

3 In winter, green schools are heated by —

Ⓐ a generator

Ⓑ electricity

Ⓒ oil

Ⓓ solar energy

GO ON ➡

4 How do chickens help the Goodwillie students make money for environmental projects?

A Their feathers are used to make coats.

B The chickens' eggs are sold in the store.

C The chickens are sold at the market.

D The chickens work as carrier pigeons.

5 The chickens at Goodwillie help the school garden by —

A providing manure

B planting seeds

C finding worms

D eating bugs

6 What is the section called "The Great Outdoors" mostly about?

A What students do to raise chickens

B Where the Goodwillie students live

C How the students learn about nature

D Why people started the Goodwillie School

7 The main goal of green schools is to teach students about —

A how to raise animals

B getting along in the classroom

C how to protect the earth

D farming in the city

Student Name _____

8 Read this sentence from the article.

Students also <u>donate</u> money or time to environmental groups.

Which word from a thesaurus means about the same as the word <u>donate</u>?

(A) Take

(B) Collect

(C) Save

(D) Give

9 Read this sentence from the article.

Some <u>members</u> of a third-grade class are working on a project that will last about two years.

In this sentence, the word <u>members</u> means about the same as —

(A) students

(B) plants

(C) classrooms

(D) groups

GO ON ▶

10 At the Goodwillie School, what lessons do students learn through farming and raising chickens? Explain your answer and support it with details from the article.

_____

_____

_____

_____

_____

_____

_____

STOP

Selection Test

Wolf!

DIRECTIONS
Decide which is the best answer to each question.

1 How is the wolf in this story different from a wolf in real life?

(A) He gets very hungry.

(B) He jumps over a fence.

(C) He howls at other animals.

(D) He walks on two legs and talks.

2 The duck, the pig, and the cow are different from other animals in the story because they —

(A) talk together

(B) read books

(C) live on a farm

(D) run for their lives

3 Just after the animals tell the wolf to leave, he —

(A) goes to school to learn to read

(B) finds some other friends

(C) buys his own book

(D) goes on a picnic with the animals

4 How are the duck, the pig, and the cow alike?

(A) They are hard to please.

(B) They are afraid of the wolf.

(C) They like to make new friends.

(D) They want to help the wolf.

GO ON ➡

5 Why do the farm animals ask the wolf to go on a picnic?

  A They want him to buy food for them.

  B They like the way he reads stories.

  C They are getting ready to eat him.

  D They have no more books to read.

6 Which word best describes the wolf?

  A Foolish

  B Angry

  C Shy

  D Smart

7 Read this sentence from the story.

"I can't <u>concentrate</u> on my book."

Which meaning best fits the way <u>concentrate</u> is used in this sentence?

  A Look over quickly

  B Make something thick

  C Pay closer attention

  D Try to forget about

8 Read this sentence.

The wolf bought a splendid new storybook.

The word splendid means —

- **A** difficult
- **B** tiny
- **C** curving
- **D** wonderful

9 Read this sentence from the story.

He would read so well that the farm animals would admire him.

What does the word admire mean?

- **A** Fear
- **B** Respect
- **C** Attack
- **D** Be friends with

GO ON

10 How can the reader tell that the farm animals like the wolf at the end of the story? Explain your answer and support it with details from the story.

_____

_____

_____

_____

_____

_____

My Very Own Room

DIRECTIONS
Decide which is the best answer to each question.

1 Why does the girl sit in a tree in the beginning of the story?

   A It is too cold in the basement.

   B She hides her books in the branches.

   C She needs a place of her own to think.

   D Her brothers are too small to reach her up there.

2 Why doesn't the girl's mother want her to use the storage closet at first?

   A Many things are stored in there.

   B There is no more paint for the walls.

   C It is too close to the kitchen.

   D It has no windows.

3 Before Tío Pancho brings the bed, the family has to —

   A put blue stamps in a book

   B sell the crate to pay for the bed

   C measure the wall space with yarn

   D wait for him to return from Mexico

4 Which of these items is placed in the girl's new room?

   A A table

   B A lamp

   C A chair

   D A bookshelf

GO ON

5 Why will the girl probably enjoy reading to her youngest brothers more in the future?

- **A** They have learned how to read.
- **B** Her family has moved to a bigger home.
- **C** They are her two favorite brothers.
- **D** She has a place of her own.

6 How can the reader tell that the family in this story cares for one another?

- **A** They work together to clear space for the girl.
- **B** They cook a huge meal together.
- **C** They play pranks on each other all day long.
- **D** They all go to the park together.

7 Read this sentence from the story.

"And we could put a tarp on top so nothing would get ruined," I added.

Which meaning best fits the way ruined is used in this sentence?

- **A** Damaged or harmed
- **B** Losing one's health, position or fortune
- **C** A destruction or wreck
- **D** Remains from an ancient city

8 Read this sentence from the story.

The next day I went to our public library and rushed home with my arms full of books, six to be <u>exact</u>.

What is the meaning of the word <u>exact</u> as it is used in the sentence?

A Expensive

B Silly

C Important

D Correct

9 Read this sentence.

The girl in the story felt like the <u>luckiest</u> girl in the world.

The word <u>luckiest</u> means —

A before luck

B most lucky

C having no luck

D one who is lucky

10 If the girl in the story needs a new dress for a special event, what will the family most likely do? Explain your answer and support it with details from the story.

_____

_____

_____

_____

_____

_____

Boom Town

DIRECTIONS
Decide which is the best answer to each question.

1 Read the chart below.

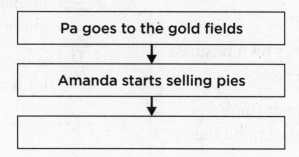

Which of the following belongs in the empty box?

A Amanda picks some berries.

B Peddler Pete opens a store.

C Ma finds a big cabin.

D Pa takes a bath and sings.

2 Why does Amanda's family move to California?

    A A tornado destroys their old home.

    B Amanda wants to start a pie business.

    C They want to find gold and get rich.

    D They have family in California.

3 What happens the first time Amanda makes a pie in her new home?

    A It is perfect.

    B The dog eats it.

    C She sells it to the banker.

    D It turns as hard as a rock.

4 Why doesn't Ma have time to help Amanda bake pies at first?

- **A** She is going to have a baby.
- **B** She is too busy looking for gold.
- **C** She has her own business selling dresses.
- **D** She does not think Amanda is a good baker.

5 What happens just before Mr. Hooper agrees to help build sidewalks for the new town?

- **A** Amanda agrees to use his new bank.
- **B** The old sidewalks break.
- **C** Amanda falls into the mud.
- **D** Cowboy Charlie opens a stable.

6 The town is a boom town because —

- **A** it is a loud place
- **B** it grows very quickly
- **C** people make gunpowder there
- **D** someone hears a loud boom

7 Read this sentence.

Amanda's brothers grumbled when she asked them to help her.

The word grumbled means —

- **A** ran away
- **B** moaned in pain
- **C** worked long and hard
- **D** complained in a low voice

GO ON

8 Read this sentence.

Baby Betsy <u>wailed</u> like a coyote.

Which word means about the same thing as <u>wailed</u>?

A) Fell

B) Cried

C) Waited

D) Laughed

9 Read this sentence from the story.

It took us twenty-one days on the <u>stagecoach</u> to get to California.

What does the word <u>stagecoach</u> mean?

A) A place for putting on plays

B) A person who leads a team

C) A wagon pulled by horses

D) A town where people live in tents

10 Tell, in order, how the town got a school and a church. Support your answer with details from the story.

_____

_____

_____

_____

_____

_____

_____

Selection Test

Home-Grown Butterflies

DIRECTIONS
Decide which is the best answer to each question.

1 Look at the chart below.

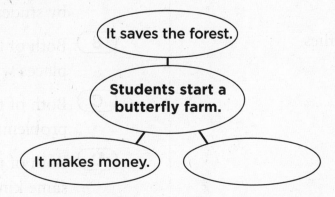

Which of these details belongs in the empty oval?

A It brings back the fish.

B It makes local zoos angry.

C It keeps students from going to class.

D It lets them buy more school supplies.

---

2 Why was the butterfly farm in Costa Rica created?

A The villagers needed a new way to make money.

B A company offered the villagers a lot of money.

C Butterfly catching was an old Costa Rican custom.

D The rain forest had too many butterflies.

3 Why do the students need to watch out for chickens?

A The chickens scare the butterflies.

B The chickens eat the worms from the garden.

C Chickens are not allowed near the school.

D The school principal is afraid of chickens.

GO ON ▶

4 What do the zoos buy from the butterfly farms?

- **A** Worms
- **B** Flowers
- **C** Pupae
- **D** Butterflies

5 When they grow up, the students in Costa Rica most likely will —

- **A** become fishermen
- **B** move to San Diego
- **C** write about their butterfly experience
- **D** try to help protect the environment

6 Which of these is most likely true about the butterfly farm at the school in Costa Rica and the one in California?

- **A** Both of them are run by students.
- **B** Both of them are in places with cold weather.
- **C** Both of them have problems with chickens.
- **D** Both of them raise the same kinds of butterflies.

7 Read this sentence.

A farm needs to have a steady supply of wild butterflies to succeed.

The word supply means that the butterflies are —

- **A** expensive
- **B** not needed
- **C** old-fashioned
- **D** available to use

GO ON

Selection Test

8 Read this sentence from the article.

They've learned from the kids how to use the forest without <u>harming</u> it.

The word <u>harming</u> means —

  A hurting

  B picking

  C growing

  D watching

9 Read this sentence from the article.

But then, because of pollution and overfishing, the fish began to <u>disappear</u>.

What does the word <u>disappear</u> mean?

  A Move closer

  B Increase in size

  C Go out of sight

  D Appear quickly

10 How have the students in Costa Rica helped their community? Explain your answer and support it with details from the article.

_____

_____

_____

_____

_____

_____

_____

_____

Go West!

DIRECTIONS
Decide which is the best answer to each question.

1 What is this article mostly about?

   (A) Why railroads took so long to build

   (B) What you can see at the Museum of American Railroads

   (C) How railroads changed the Southwest

   (D) Where each railroad in America began and ended

2 The completion of the first transcontinental railroad helped people to —

   (A) find good jobs in the West

   (B) travel to the West faster

   (C) prepare more traditional foods

   (D) become friends with Native Americans

3 The railroads wanted people to settle in the West because —

   (A) it was good for business

   (B) the East was too crowded

   (C) some towns were not so lucky

   (D) life in the West was dangerous

4 Which city began as a camp for railway workers?

   (A) New York City

   (B) Odessa, Texas

   (C) San Francisco

   (D) Dallas, Texas

GO ON ➤

5 In the late 1800s, many people traveled to the Southwest because —

   A there were no businesses

   B food was scarce

   C Native Americans lived there

   D land was cheap

6 Many railroad lines to the West were built by workers from —

   A France

   B England

   C China

   D Germany

7 How did the railroads help mining industries grow in the Southwest?

   A They connected mines with factories.

   B They changed ways of farming.

   C They brought new foods and music.

   D They added dining cars to trains.

GO ON

8 Read this sentence from the article.

That's how the city of Odessa, Texas, was <u>established</u>.

Which word from the section "New Towns" means the opposite of <u>established</u>?

- **A** *lucky*
- **B** *disappeared*
- **C** *built*
- **D** *important*

9 Read this sentence from the article.

Before long, new <u>communities</u> began to form along the train lines.

What does the word <u>communities</u> mean?

- **A** Churches
- **B** Walls
- **C** Battles
- **D** Towns

GO ON ▶

10 How did railroads help farmers and ranchers in the Southwest? Explain your answer and support it with details from the article.

_____

_____

_____

_____

_____

_____

_____

Selection Test

Here's My Dollar

DIRECTIONS
Decide which is the best answer to each question.

1 Why did Angel write a letter?

A She read about the needs of the zoo.

B She saw a news program about the local zoos.

C She met a worker at the zoo who wanted to fix the seal pool.

D She heard her great-grandmother talking about the zoo's problems.

2 Why did Angel send her letter to *The Fresno Bee*?

A She hoped people would read it and help the zoo.

B Her mother worked for *The Fresno Bee*.

C The newspaper company owned the zoo.

D It was closer to her home than the zoo was.

3 Which word best describes Angel?

A Caring

B Angry

C Shy

D Sad

4 The author probably wrote this article to —

A teach a lesson about having pets

B give information about Angel Arellano

C explain how to raise money

D tell a funny story about animals

5 Angel shows that she is daring when she —

(A) walks along a monkey platform

(B) feeds an apple to a giraffe

(C) helps rebuild the rain forest bridge

(D) takes a ride on a camel

6 Angel appeared on a television show to —

(A) sell some special t-shirts

(B) feed animals from the zoo

(C) tell people about Fresno

(D) raise money for the zoo

7 Why does the author say in the article that a hero is four feet two inches tall?

(A) Only short people can be heroes.

(B) Angel is four feet two inches tall.

(C) The author doesn't like tall people.

(D) A giraffe is four feet two inches tall.

GO ON ➡

8 Read this sentence from the article.

The people at the Chaffee Zoo were thrilled.

The word thrilled means —

- **A** very excited
- **B** disappointed
- **C** very surprised
- **D** relieved

9 Read this sentence.

"Give a dollar, save a life" is an example of a slogan.

What does the word slogan mean?

- **A** A poem that uses rhyming words
- **B** A fact about animals
- **C** A phrase that is easy to remember
- **D** A name for a business

GO ON

10 How did Angel spread the word about her campaign to raise money for the zoo? Explain your answer and support it with details and information from the article.

_____

_____

_____

_____

_____

_____

_____

_____

A Castle on Viola Street

DIRECTIONS
Decide which is the best answer to each question.

1 Where is Andy when he sees the flier about the meeting to own a home?

  A In the park

  B At the Soap & Go

  C In the library

  D At school

2 Why does Andy's dad tell him that sometimes new things are hard to get used to and people are slow to change?

  A Andy's sisters refuse to help in building the houses.

  B The family waiting for their house decides to move somewhere else.

  C The organization building the houses decides to build a mall instead.

  D Some people in the neighborhood do not want to accept the new houses.

3 Why does Andy's family sign up to help fix houses for other people?

  A Their dad gets a new job.

  B They hope to get a house one day.

  C Andy wants to become a builder.

  D The neighborhood houses need repair.

4 Just after the Tran family moves into their new house, they —

  A have a potluck supper

  B adopt a dog as a pet

  C repaint their walls

  D build a swimming pool

GO ON ➡

5 Which sentence expresses the main theme of this story?

(A) Animals can be helpful, too.

(B) It is important to think about the past.

(C) People can reach their dreams by working hard.

(D) People should be more open to new experiences.

6 The reader can tell from this story that Andy is —

(A) lonely

(B) frustrated

(C) disappointed

(D) hardworking

7 What is the result of Andy's family's hard work?

(A) The family gets a lot of money.

(B) Andy finishes the family's laundry.

(C) The family gets a house.

(D) Andy builds a birdhouse.

8 Read this sentence.

Mr. and Mrs. Rivera look forward to living in a place that does not have leaky pipes.

What does the word leaky mean?

A Very cold

B Changing in size

C Completely empty

D Allowing liquid to escape

9 Read this sentence from the story.

The kitchen had shiny linoleum floors and brand-new appliances.

The word appliances means —

A plates for the kitchen

B hammers and nails

C pieces of equipment

D ways of doing things

© Macmillan/McGraw-Hill

GO ON

10 Why is this story called "A Castle on Viola Street"? Explain your answer and
support it with details from the story.

_____

_____

_____

_____

_____

_____

_____

Author: A True Story

DIRECTIONS
Decide which is the best answer to each question.

1 What is the main topic of this article?

   A A Fizzle Box

   B The author's life

   C Mirror writing

   D The grocery list

2 When Helen Lester was a child, she —

   A played lots of sports

   B bought the groceries

   C wrote everything backwards

   D liked math in school

3 What was Helen Lester's first job?

   A A writer

   B An artist

   C A teacher

   D A circus performer

4 Why did Helen Lester write her seventh book?

   A She had a lot of good ideas.

   B The first six books were rejected.

   C Her students asked her to write more books.

   D Her publisher asked her to write more books.

GO ON ➡

5 What was the author's purpose for writing the article?

  A To persuade readers to become writers

  B To tell how she learned to write as a child

  C To complain about how hard it is to be a writer

  D To inform readers about what it's like to be a writer

6 Which word best describes Helen Lester?

  A Hardworking

  B Frustrated

  C Angry

  D Sad

7 Where does Helen Lester keep her unfinished ideas?

  A In her Fizzle Box

  B In a notebook

  C On her desk

  D In her car

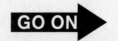

8 Read this sentence from the article.

Thanks to a lot of help, I was finally able to write in the proper direction.

Which word means the opposite of proper?

A Right

B Usual

C Quick

D Wrong

9 Read this sentence from the article.

I was beside myself with joy and excitement.

The word excitement means —

A worry

B happiness

C boredom

D sadness

10 How does Helen Lester feel about being a writer? Explain your answer and support it with details from the article.

_____

_____

_____

_____

_____

_____

_____

Dear Juno

DIRECTIONS
Decide which is the best answer to each question.

1 Look at the web below.

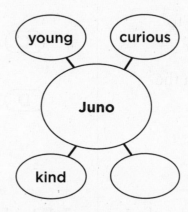

Which of these belongs in the empty oval?

A Loud

B Shy

C Rude

D Smart

2 Why does Juno watch planes?

A There is nothing else for him to do.

B He wants to be a pilot when he grows up.

C He is thinking about his grandmother in Korea.

D He is waiting for his grandmother to arrive.

3 What does Juno find in the letter from his grandmother?

A A dried flower and a picture

B A large leaf

C A pencil and a small book

D A toy kitten

GO ON

4 Juno figures out what his grandmother's letter says by —

(A) learning Korean

(B) asking his parents to read it to him

(C) taking the letter to school with him

(D) using clues from the things she sent

5 After Juno takes his grandmother's letter to school, he decides to —

(A) take a trip

(B) learn to read and write Korean

(C) play with Sam

(D) write a letter to his grandmother

6 What does Juno know when he finds the toy plane in his grandmother's letter?

(A) He is going to Korea.

(B) It will soon be his birthday.

(C) His grandmother is coming to visit.

(D) His grandmother has learned to make toys.

7 Why does Juno draw pictures instead of writing a letter to his grandmother?

(A) Juno and his grandmother do not speak the same language.

(B) Juno likes pictures better than words.

(C) Juno's grandmother cannot read.

(D) Juno does not know how to write.

GO ON ➡

Selection Test

8 Read the sentence from the story.

He pulled out the photograph.

Which word means about the same thing as the word photograph?

- **A** Message
- **B** Music
- **C** Picture
- **D** Plane

9 Read the sentence from the story.

Juno's father looked in the envelope.

The word envelope means —

- **A** a large room
- **B** something that holds a letter
- **C** a cardboard box
- **D** something that makes you sleepy

GO ON

10 What things will Grandma recognize when she comes to visit? Explain your answer and support it with details from the story.

_____

_____

_____

_____

_____

_____

_____

Messaging Mania

DIRECTIONS
Decide which is the best answer to each question.

1 Some people feel that Instant Messaging can be a great tool for —

   A parents

   B communication

   C wasting time

   D keeping busy

2 In Instant Messaging, words get shortened and new slang is invented because IM users —

   A are poor spellers

   B make mistakes as they type

   C type very fast

   D want to keep their messages secret

3 According to the article, how often do many kids IM each other?

   A Every day

   B Once a month

   C Twice a week

   D Every hour

4 Parents and teachers are afraid that when children spend too much time on the computer, it takes time away from —

   A cooking meals

   B cleaning their rooms

   C seeing friends

   D studying and playing outdoors

GO ON

5 Researchers note that parents worry about their kids and the Internet because —

(A) kids play too many video games

(B) new technology makes adults nervous

(C) some kids sit and wait for IMs

(D) teachers get upset when kids use slang

6 Some people think that IMing can make kids better students because it —

(A) makes them read more books

(B) keeps them in the house

(C) doesn't run up the phone bill

(D) helps them learn to type

7 Read this sentence from the article.

They may get fast enough to break a speed-typing record!

Which meaning of record best fits the way it is used in this sentence?

(A) To remember or recall

(B) To tape or make note of

(C) An official list of achievements

(D) A disk that has music on it

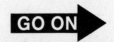

Selection Test

8 Read this sentence from the article.

Studies <u>estimate</u> that most IM sessions last more than half an hour.

The word <u>estimate</u> means —

A guess

B state

C remember

D accept

9 Read this sentence.

Some kids <u>focus</u> more on IMing friends than on anything else.

The word <u>focus</u> means —

A avoid carefully

B pay attention to

C share together

D have fun with

GO ON

10 Why is it best only to write things in an IM that you would say to a friend in person? Explain your answer and support it with details from the article.

_____

_____

_____

_____

_____

_____

_____

STOP

Selection Test

What Do Illustrators Do?

DIRECTIONS
Decide which is the best answer to each question.

1 What is the first thing an illustrator does when working on a book?

  A Finds people to act as models

  B Makes a dummy of the book

  C Chooses which scenes to illustrate

  D Makes a sketch of each picture

2 How does one of the illustrators make her story of *Jack and the Beanstalk* different?

  A She changes the ending.

  B She gets rid of the beanstalk.

  C She changes Jack's name to Jim.

  D She makes the main character a girl.

3 How does one illustrator show how fast the beanstalk grows?

  A He rewrites the story.

  B He puts in a cat for scale.

  C He shows a bird's-eye view.

  D He uses a mouse's-eye view.

4 An illustrator would use a mirror while drawing to —

  A see how different expressions look

  B sketch objects behind him or her

  C trace the shape of the mirror

  D take a break from drawing

5 When do the editor and designer make suggestions?

   A After the illustrator does the cover

   B Before the illustrator makes a plan

   C After the illustrator makes a dummy

   D Before the illustrator sketches the illustrations

6 When do illustrators usually work on the cover of the book?

   A Last

   B After the book has been published

   C First

   D Before they have finished the dummy

7 Read this sentence.

The artist liked to <u>illustrate</u> fun stories.

Which word means about the same thing as <u>illustrate</u>?

   A Tell

   B Buy

   C Draw

   D Write

8 Read this sentence.

The store sold paper with different <u>textures</u>.

What does the word <u>textures</u> mean?

(A) The sizes of drawings

(B) Numbers of words on a page

(C) Colors made by artists

(D) How things feel when you touch them

9 Read this sentence.

She was famous for her <u>style</u> of painting.

What does the word <u>style</u> mean as it is used in the sentence?

(A) The artist's age

(B) A type of pencil

(C) A way of doing something

(D) How much something costs

© Macmillan/McGraw-Hill

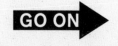

10 What is the difference between an illustrator and an illustrator who is an author? Explain your answer and support it with details from the article.

_____

_____

_____

_____

_____

_____

_____

Selection Test

The Jones Family Express

DIRECTIONS
Decide which is the best answer to each question.

1 Look at the chart below.

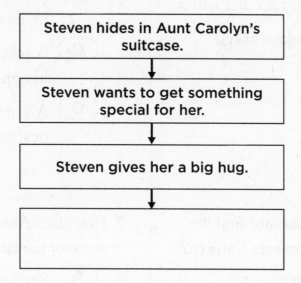

Which of these belongs in the empty box?

A Aunt Carolyn tells funny stories.

B Steven is scared of Aunt Carolyn.

C Aunt Carolyn doesn't like to come home.

D Steven really likes Aunt Carolyn.

---

2 What has the narrator always wanted to do?

A Have a block party

B Go shopping at the mall

C Travel with his aunt

D Visit his cousin's house

3 What does Aunt Carolyn send to the narrator?

A Candy

B Photos

C Toy trains

D Postcards

GO ON ➡

4 Why does the narrator want to get a present for Aunt Carolyn?

- **A** It is her birthday.
- **B** The party is for her.
- **C** He doesn't see her often.
- **D** His grandma asked him to.

6 What does the narrator give to Aunt Carolyn?

- **A** A toy train with photos of his family
- **B** A postcard from where he has been
- **C** A picture frame with his photo
- **D** A bottle of her favorite perfume

5 Where does the narrator find the perfect present for Aunt Carolyn?

- **A** The train station
- **B** Ms. Ruby's shop
- **C** Perkins Drugstore
- **D** Uncle Charles's house

7 How does Aunt Carolyn give the narrator the best present of all?

- **A** She sends him new postcards.
- **B** She lets him travel with her.
- **C** She gives him a toy train.
- **D** She buys all the children ice cream.

© Macmillan/McGraw-Hill

8 Read this sentence.

The store was full of <u>expensive</u> things that he could not buy.

What does the word <u>expensive</u> mean as it is used in the sentence?

- **A** Brand-new
- **B** Broken
- **C** Very cheap
- **D** Costly

9 Read this sentence.

Aunt Carolyn took the <u>wrapping</u> off the package.

Which word from the story is a homophone for the word <u>wrapping</u>?

- **A** *rapping*
- **B** *opening*
- **C** *roping*
- **D** *present*

GO ON ➤

10 What made Sean more special than everyone else at the block party? Explain your answer and support it with details from the story.

_____

_____

_____

_____

_____

_____

_____

Seven Spools of Thread

DIRECTIONS
Decide which is the best answer to each question.

1 What does the father want his sons to do before they have their inheritance?

(A) Return from their vacation

(B) Buy more spools of thread

(C) Make enough money to keep the farm running

(D) Prove that they can work together and get along

2 What happens last in the story?

(A) The brothers discuss what to do with the thread.

(B) The brothers sell their cloth to the King's treasurer.

(C) The seven brothers work together farming their land.

(D) The Chief tells the brothers about their father's wishes.

3 What is the main theme in this story?

(A) People can achieve more by working together.

(B) Having too many brothers will cause confusion.

(C) Taking care of a farm is difficult work.

(D) Always look before you leap.

4 Why is the cloth made by the seven brothers unusual?

(A) It smells like apples.

(B) It contains gold nuggets.

(C) It contains many colors.

(D) It is smaller than most cloths.

GO ON

5 How do the brothers make gold from silk threads?

- **A** They use only the gold thread.
- **B** They melt the thread and it turns into gold.
- **C** They find tiny nuggets of gold in the thread.
- **D** They sell the cloth they make from the thread for gold.

6 How do the seven brothers change in this story?

- **A** They begin working together peacefully.
- **B** The oldest brother becomes the new leader.
- **C** The youngest brother goes on vacation.
- **D** The seven brothers grow angrier.

7 Read this sentence.

The seven brothers were always quarreling.

Which word means about the same thing as the word quarreling?

- **A** Eating
- **B** Asking
- **C** Fighting
- **D** Studying

© Macmillan/McGraw-Hill

8 Read this sentence.

Cloth fit for a king should be purchased at a price only a king can pay.

The word purchased means —

(A) received as a gift

(B) bought with money

(C) sold at the market

(D) given away for free

9 Read this sentence from the story.

And so it would continue until the moon beamed down and the stars twinkled in the sky.

Which meaning from a dictionary best fits the way beamed is used in this sentence?

(A) Shone brightly

(B) Piece of wood

(C) Faded away

(D) Fell downward

GO ON

10 How do the seven brothers help the other villagers? Explain your answer and support it with details from the story.

_____

_____

_____

_____

_____

_____

Selection Test

Nacho and Lolita

DIRECTIONS
Decide which is the best answer to each question.

1 When Nacho first arrives at San Juan Capistrano, he thinks that everything is —

  A cold and cruel

  B quiet and wonderful

  C dull and brown

  D colorful and exciting

2 Why does Nacho carry a branch with him for the long trip over the ocean?

  A It is his lucky charm.

  B It will scare away predators.

  C He can use it as a peace offering when they arrive.

  D He can use it to float on when he gets tired.

3 Why do Lolita and her chicks have to leave the Mission San Juan Capistrano?

  A Summer is coming and it will be too hot.

  B Nothing grows there and everything is brown.

  C Winter is coming and it will be too cold.

  D The other birds at the mission are mean to them.

4 Why does Nacho pluck all his beautifully colored feathers?

  A He is tired of looking different from the other birds.

  B He plans to sell them at the mission.

  C He thinks he will be able to fly better.

  D He wants to plant them so colorful things will grow.

GO ON ➡

© Macmillan/McGraw-Hill

5 When Nacho is no longer colorful, Lolita thinks that he —

A is showing off

B is as splendid as always

C looks ridiculous

D should get his colors back

6 How do the swallows find their way back to Capistrano in the spring?

A They get detailed instructions from Nacho.

B They are attracted to the colorful flowers and trees.

C They follow the sound of the mission bell.

D They never find their way back to Capistrano.

7 When the swallows return, Nacho is worried that Lolita won't like him anymore because —

A he doesn't live in a nice nest

B she has been away so long

C he is drab and colorless

D she knows he cannot fly very far

Selection Test

8 Read this sentence from the story.

"Stay with me," he <u>pleaded</u>.

Which word from a thesaurus is a synonym for <u>pleaded</u>?

A Laughed

B Ignored

C Begged

D Celebrated

9 Read this sentence.

Nacho was so full with <u>affection</u> and purpose.

Which word from a thesaurus is a synonym for <u>affection</u>?

A Love

B Hatred

C Courage

D Confusion

GO ON

10 What is the main theme, or message, in this story? Explain your answer and support it with details from the story.

_____

_____

_____

_____

_____

_____

A Growing Interest

DIRECTIONS
Decide which is the best answer to each question.

1 According to this article, kids from big cities like Houston may not know —

A how to read magazines and newspapers

B where to buy fruits and vegetables

C how the food they eat is grown

D where they can see wild animals

2 Urban Harvest helps people by teaching them about —

A community gardening

B health care

C traveling safely

D saving money

3 The people who work for Urban Harvest are —

A farmers

B volunteers

C teachers

D students

4 What do kids and teachers at the Cedarbrook Elementary School do in July?

A Plant beans

B Read books

C Write lists

D Pick corn

GO ON ➡

5 Having a community garden can help a neighborhood by —

A raising food prices

B making it beautiful

C getting rid of trash

D attracting wild birds

6 What can students learn from helping with a community garden?

A How nature works

B Why cities grow

C What food costs

D Where birds go

7 At Eugene Field Elementary in Tulsa, Oklahoma, kids who work on a school garden learn writing skills by —

A sending letters

B reading directions

C making signs

D keeping journals

GO ON ➡

Selection Test

8 Read this sentence from the article.

Gardening helps students learn how easy it is to eat healthful foods.

The word <u>healthful</u> means —

- **A** before health
- **B** without health
- **C** good for one's health
- **D** one who is healthy

9 Read this sentence.

People can <u>utilize</u> those skills to create gardens.

Which word from the article means the same thing as the word <u>utilize</u>?

- **A** *solve*
- **B** *use*
- **C** *grow*
- **D** *build*

GO ON ➡

10 How do school gardens help people in Houston eat better food? Explain your answer and support it with details from the article.

_____

_____

_____

_____

_____

_____

Ramona and Her Father

DIRECTIONS
Decide which is the best answer to each question.

1 Look at the chart below.

Solutions
Beezus will baby-sit.
Mrs. Quimby takes a full-time job.
Mr. Quimby looks for a job.
Ramona plans to make a million dollars.

↓

Problem
_____

Which of these belongs on the blank line?

A The Quimbys have nothing to eat for dinner.

B Ramona is driving Beezus crazy.

C Mr. Quimby has lost his job.

D Mr. and Mrs. Quimby have an argument.

---

2 What is the one item that Ramona leaves on her Christmas list?

A *ginny pigs*

B *one happy family*

C *new job for Father*

D *Christmas books*

3 Why did Mr. Quimby lose his job?

A He was fired for coming in late too often.

B He didn't like it and decided to quit.

C He was offered a better job that he wanted more.

D A big company took over his company and let some people go.

GO ON

4 Mr. Quimby can't take Ramona to the park any longer because he —

  A has to wait by the phone in case someone calls

  B is so worried about a job that he doesn't love her anymore

  C has a new job cleaning houses in their neighborhood

  D thinks that Ramona should practice to be on television

5 What is the solution to the family's problem that Ramona comes up with at the end of the story?

  A She will practice to be in a television commercial.

  B She will go to work at Whopperburger.

  C She and Beezus will make rose-scented perfume.

  D She and her friend Howie will open a lemonade stand.

6 What would Ramona like to do with a million dollars?

  A Eat caramel apples every day of the week

  B Go to see the elephants at the zoo

  C Buy a cuckoo clock for every room in the house

  D Eat bread and margarine while wearing a crown

7 At the beginning of the story, how can Beezus tell that something is wrong?

  A Ramona is crying.

  B The neighbors are acting oddly.

  C Her parents are whispering.

  D Her father won't stop laughing.

GO ON

Selection Test

8 Read this sentence.

Unfortunately, the perfume Ramona tried to make always smelled like rotten rose petals.

The word unfortunately means —

- **A** with happiness
- **B** without luck
- **C** with fortune
- **D** without money

9 Read this sentence from the story.

When she was cross with Beezus, she laid her sister's place mat face down.

What does the word cross mean in this sentence?

- **A** Upset or angry
- **B** Pleased
- **C** Teasing or joking
- **D** Friendly

GO ON ➤

10 In what ways does Ramona think she might be able to earn some money for the family? Explain your answer and support it with details from the story.

_____

_____

_____

_____

_____

_____

Out of this World!

DIRECTIONS
Decide which is the best answer to each question.

1

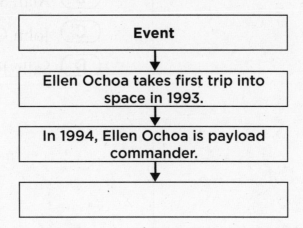

Which of these belongs in the empty box?

A Sally Ride goes into space in 1983.

B Ellen Ochoa begins college at Stanford.

C Gordon Cooer stays in orbit more than 24 hours.

D Ellen Ochoa walks in space and works on the ISS.

2 What did Ellen Ochoa plan to be when she first went to college?

A A musician

B An athlete

C An astronaut

D A teacher

3 One unique thing about Ellen Ochoa is that she was the —

A first female Hispanic astronaut

B only woman ever to go into space

C first woman to walk on the moon

D youngest astronaut in history

4 The different shapes the moon seems to take on are called —

    (A) orbits

    (B) shadows

    (C) phases

    (D) quarters

6 Who was the first American astronaut to orbit Earth?

    (A) Neil Armstrong

    (B) Alan Shepard

    (C) John Glenn

    (D) Sally Ride

5 What does Ellen Ochoa find odd about weightlessness?

    (A) It feels like swimming.

    (B) It makes her tired.

    (C) It makes her feel sick.

    (D) It feels so natural.

7 In the early years of the space program, there were no women astronauts because they —

    (A) didn't have the math and science skills

    (B) were not allowed to apply to the program

    (C) couldn't afford to enter the program

    (D) didn't care about going into space

GO ON ▶

8 Read this sentence.

The astronaut was a <u>specialist</u> in the field of robots.

Which word means about the same thing as <u>specialist</u>?

(A) Teacher

(B) Expert

(C) Beginner

(D) Pilot

9 Read this sentence.

The commander makes the crucial <u>decisions</u>.

Which word from a thesaurus means the same as the word <u>decisions</u>?

(A) Trips

(B) Changes

(C) Goals

(D) Choices

GO ON

10 According to Ellen Ochoa, what skills or traits are most important for an astronaut? Explain your answer and support it with details from the article.

_____

_____

_____

_____

_____

_____

_____

Penguin Chick

DIRECTIONS
Decide which is the best answer to each question.

1 Look at the chart below.

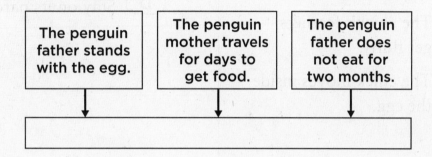

Which main idea belongs in the empty box?

A The penguin mother walks or slides on her belly across the ice.

B Emperor penguins work hard to take care of their chicks in Antarctica.

C Most birds build nests for their eggs, but emperor penguins do not.

D Penguin mothers lay only one egg each year in the cold Antarctic.

---

2 Why don't penguins in Antarctica build nests?

A There is nothing to build nests with.

B They are only there for a short time.

C Their eggs will never hatch in a nest.

D They are too lazy to make nests.

3 Soon after she lays an egg, the penguin mother leaves to —

A find food

B find another mate

C get some exercise

D go someplace warmer

4 Which of these happens last when a chick hatches?

- **A** The egg cracks open.
- **B** The chick pecks and pecks.
- **C** The chick's feathers get fluffy.
- **D** The chick moves inside the egg.

5 What happens when the mother returns?

- **A** The father stays by her side.
- **B** The chick travels to open water.
- **C** The mother stays for only a short time.
- **D** The mothers feeds and cares for the chick.

6 What can a junior penguin do?

- **A** Build a nest
- **B** Travel to the ocean
- **C** Get food for its parents
- **D** Stay on its parents' feet

7 What problem do emperor penguins face during their time in Antarctica?

- **A** They must go for long periods without food.
- **B** They cannot find enough ice for shelter.
- **C** They must live with very hot weather in the summer.
- **D** They get lost when they fly anywhere.

GO ON

Selection Test

8 Read this sentence.

Fluffy <u>down</u> helps keep the new chicks warm in Antarctica.

Which meaning of <u>down</u> best fits the way it is used in this sentence?

(**A**) Warm skin

(**B**) Feeling sad

(**C**) To go lower

(**D**) Soft feathers

9 Read this sentence.

The penguin father <u>shuffles</u> his feet.

Which meaning of <u>shuffles</u> best fits the way it is used in this sentence?

(**A**) Acts in a careless manner

(**B**) Mixes a deck of playing cards

(**C**) Moves something from place to place

(**D**) Walks by dragging the feet

10 What kinds of problems do emperor penguins face when trying to raise chicks in Antarctica? Explain your answer and support it with details from the article.

_____

_____

_____

_____

_____

_____

_____

_____

Selection Test

Animal Homes

DIRECTIONS
Decide which is the best answer to each question.

1 Which of these best describes one reason why honeybees use honeycombs?

  A To hide from their enemies

  B To attract other honeybees

  C To stay cool on hot days

  D To take care of their young

2 Which sentence best explains why beavers are so busy?

  A A lot of work goes into building a beaver lodge.

  B Beavers do not get along well with other animals.

  C Beaver dams are usually built in the middle of a pond.

  D The beaver's main predators are wolves and river otters.

3 Which sentence best describes how a beaver lodge is different from the way it appears?

  A It looks big but is really very tiny.

  B It is always placed near a waterfall.

  C It has many holes but holds back the water.

  D It looks like a pile of sticks but is really a home underneath.

4 Which of these best describes what hermit crabs do?

  A They build nests for their young.

  B They swim quickly to escape the beavers.

  C They live with pea crabs near the surface of the ocean.

  D They search for new shells as they outgrow their old ones.

5 Which of these best describes what the cowbird does?

  A She hides her eggs in a dark cave.

  B She builds a nest in another bird's tree.

  C She lays her egg in another bird's nest.

  D She sits on her eggs until they hatch.

6 Which animal carries its home on its back?

  A Turtle

  B Spider

  C Termite

  D Beaver

7 Which animal builds its own home?

  A Pea crab

  B Bagworm

  C Hermit crab

  D Tortoise

GO ON

8 Read this sentence.

A termite tower may <u>contain</u>
millions of termites.

Which word means about the same
thing as the word <u>contain</u>?

(**A**) Count

(**B**) Show

(**C**) Hold

(**D**) Eat

9 Read this sentence.

Bees store honey in some of the
<u>cells</u> of their hive.

Which word is a homophone
for <u>cells</u>?

(**A**) Sells

(**B**) Nests

(**C**) Seals

(**D**) Kills

GO ON

10 Describe how a weaverbird builds its nest. Explain your answer and support it with details from the article.

_____

_____

_____

_____

_____

_____

_____

STOP

Call of the Wild

DIRECTIONS
Decide which is the best answer to each question.

1 Why do coyotes live in more places now than they did long ago?

   (A) They spread out to follow their food sources.

   (B) Wildlife experts introduced them into new habitats.

   (C) They spread out to find open spaces.

   (D) They needed to seek new land after a drought.

2 How does the arctic fox adapt to the Arctic winter?

   (A) It hibernates during the coldest months.

   (B) Its fur turns white to match the snow.

   (C) It grows extra padding beneath its fur to keep dry.

   (D) It has long teeth for finding insects in frozen soil.

3 How did finches from South America adapt to the Galapagos?

   (A) They grew stronger wings so they could fly farther.

   (B) Their nests did not have to be built in trees anymore.

   (C) Their beaks changed so they could get different types of food.

   (D) They lay several eggs at a time so there would be more finches.

© Macmillan/McGraw-Hill

4 Wild turkeys have moved into some suburbs because —

    A there are more bears in the woods that feed on turkeys

    B they like the food people leave in bird feeders

    C they can no longer use their wings to fly away from danger

    D there is a lot of garbage in cans and dumpsters

5 Why doesn't the loggerhead turtle migrate south anymore?

    A Global warming has made these areas too warm.

    B There are new predators in these places, such as alligators.

    C Freshwater ponds and lakes are drying up.

    D Their tails are disappearing, making it harder to swim.

6 Scientists think that adapting to changes in the environment helps animals to —

    A store food

    B travel

    C run faster

    D survive

7 Both javelinas and black bears have moved into neighborhoods to —

    A eat human foods

    B hide from enemies

    C find warmer homes

    D make better shelters

GO ON ▶

© Macmillan/McGraw-Hill

8 Read this sentence.

Animals sometimes <u>adjust</u> to changes in the environment.

Which word from the article means about the same thing as the word <u>adjust</u>?

- **A** *feed*
- **B** *adapt*
- **C** *migrate*
- **D** *thrive*

9 Read this sentence.

They can be <u>crucial</u> to an animal's existence.

The word <u>crucial</u> means —

- **A** hopeless
- **B** important
- **C** allowed
- **D** original

GO ON ➡

10 What might cause animals to leave their habitats? Explain your answer and support it with details from the article.

_____

_____

_____

_____

_____

_____

_____

Wilbur's Boast

DIRECTIONS
Decide which is the best answer to each question.

1 Where does this story take place?

A In a zoo

B In a city

C On a boat

D On a farm

2 Wilbur doesn't need to spin a web to catch his own meals because —

A pigs do not need to eat much

B Charlotte will spin a web for him

C he can hunt in the forest whenever he likes

D Zuckerman feeds him three meals a day

3 How does Charlotte compare herself to the men on the Queensborough Bridge?

A She says it is better to wait for something good than to keep rushing around.

B She thinks Wilbur should leave the farm and visit the bridge.

C She says spinning a web is harder than building a bridge.

D She thinks rushing across a bridge can be dangerous.

4 In this story, Templeton is a —

(A) pig

(B) lamb

(C) spider

(D) rat

5 What does Charlotte do after the lamb tells Wilbur that he smells?

(A) She agrees.

(B) She defends Wilbur.

(C) She offers to let Wilbur use her bath.

(D) She tells the lamb to leave the farm immediately.

6 Charlotte uses her web mainly to —

(A) catch flies to eat

(B) tease Wilbur

(C) stay away from Templeton

(D) get from place to place

7 Read this sentence from the story.

What were we talking about, Wilbur, when we were so rudely <u>interrupted</u>?

The word <u>interrupted</u> means —

(A) bragged in a loud voice

(B) whispered softly

(C) stopped from continuing

(D) became interested in something

8 Read this sentence from the story.

Templeton seized the string, passed it around the end of the pig's tail, and tied two half hitches.

Which word means about the same thing as the word seized?

(A) Grabbed

(B) Waited

(C) Felt

(D) Saw

9 Read this sentence.

A spider must rebuild the web if it becomes full of holes.

The word rebuild means —

(A) not to build

(B) one who builds

(C) build before

(D) to build again

GO ON

© Macmillan/McGraw-Hill

10 Is Wilbur happy being a pig on a farm? Explain your answer and support it with details from the story.

_____

_____

_____

_____

_____

_____

_____

_____

STOP

Unique Animals of the Southwest

DIRECTIONS
Decide which is the best answer to each question.

1 Look at the diagram below.

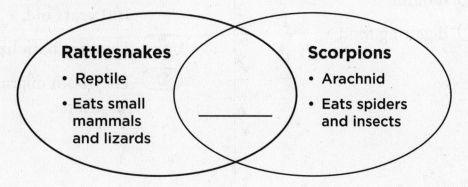

Which of these goes on the blank line?

A Found on every continent

B Uses venom to kill its prey

C Sheds its skin

D Is not dangerous to humans

2 A roadrunner uses its long
tail to —

A stay balanced

B swim in water

C clean out its nest

D carry its young

3 Where do armadillos live?

A In nests

B On top of rocks

C In burrows

D In other animals' homes

© Macmillan/McGraw-Hill

GO ON ➡

4 Rattlesnakes shake their rattles when they are —

   A threatened

   B looking for a mate

   C molting

   D digesting food

5 Where is a scorpion's stinger?

   A At the bottom of its feet

   B In its pincers

   C At the tip of its tongue

   D At the end of its tail

6 What do chuckwallas and gila monsters have in common?

   A They both give birth every 6 weeks.

   B They both live to be over 100 years old.

   C They are both lizards.

   D They both migrate in the winter.

7 A tarantula is a kind of —

   A cactus

   B spider

   C burrowing owl

   D bat

GO ON ➡

8 Read this sentence.

Nine-banded armadillos give birth to four identical babies.

Which meaning from a dictionary best fits the word identical?

A Adorable; cute

B Having bony plates

C Exactly the same

D Helpless and blind

9 Read this sentence.

Some animals have venom.

The word venom means —

A sharp teeth

B poison

C sense of smell

D stomach

GO ON

10 How are armadillos and collared peccaries alike, and how are they different? Explain your answer and support it with details from the article.

_____

_____

_____

_____

_____

_____

_____

Stone Soup

DIRECTIONS
Decide which is the best answer to each question.

1 Look at the chart below.

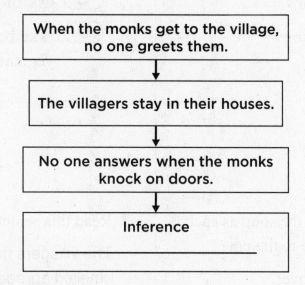

When the monks get to the village, no one greets them.

↓

The villagers stay in their houses.

↓

No one answers when the monks knock on doors.

↓

Inference

_____

Which of these belongs on the blank line?

A The villagers are all preparing for a feast.

B The monks want to make stone soup.

C The villagers do not trust strangers.

D The monks hear the sound of a bell.

2 When the monks arrive at the village, the people are —

A unfriendly

B sleeping

C starving

D kind

3 What does the little girl help the monks find?

A Stones

B Carrots

C Onions

D Mushrooms

GO ON ➡

4 What do the villagers add to the soup?

    A Tea

    B Spoons

    C Vegetables

    D Decorations

6 When the soup is ready, the villagers —

    A carry the soup home

    B sit down to eat together

    C ask the monks to leave

    D take back their vegetables

5 What happens to the soup as each person adds more to the pot?

    A It spills over.

    B It tastes more like stones.

    C It gets thicker and harder to stir.

    D It grows richer and smells better.

7 Read this sentence.

The villagers thought the soup smelled <u>agreeable</u>.

Which word means about the same thing as the word <u>agreeable</u>?

    A Awful

    B Strong

    C Smoky

    D Pleasant

GO ON

8 Read this sentence.

Everyone gathered for the
banquet that night.

What does the word
banquet mean?

- Ⓐ Small snack
- Ⓑ Pot of stones
- Ⓒ Blanket for a picnic
- Ⓓ Large meal

9 Read this sentence.

The monks were <u>guests</u> in
the village.

What does the word <u>guests</u> mean?

- Ⓐ People who come to visit
- Ⓑ Workers on a farm
- Ⓒ People who are wise and old
- Ⓓ Men who can cook

GO ON ▶

10 Why do the monks show the villagers how to make stone soup?
Explain your answer and support it with details from the story.

_____

_____

_____

_____

_____

_____

_____

The Strongest One

DIRECTIONS
Decide which is the best answer to each question.

1 Which of these is a character in the play?

(A) Moon

(B) Wind

(C) River

(D) Bear

2 Little Red Ant wants to find out who is the strongest so he can —

(A) stay near the strongest one

(B) fight the strongest one

(C) learn to be stronger

(D) know everything

3 Why is Wind stronger than Sun?

(A) Wind moves Sun around.

(B) Wind eats holes in Sun.

(C) Wind breaks Sun into pieces.

(D) Wind covers Sun's face with clouds.

4 Who is stronger than Big Rock?

(A) Little Red Ant, who can take pieces away

(B) Arrow, who can strike it

(C) Deer, who can climb on top of it

(D) Fire, who can burn it

GO ON ➡

5 Which of these gives the best summary of what Little Red Ant does in this story?

  A He sits and talks with the other ants in their home.

  B He waits in his hole to ask Sand, "Who is strongest of all?"

  C He fights other characters to see if they are the strongest.

  D He goes out and asks other characters, "Who is strongest?"

6 How is Little Red Ant like a person?

  A He wears a shirt and shoes.

  B He writes and reads.

  C He walks on two legs.

  D He talks to other characters.

7 Who is stronger than Fire?

  A Water

  B Stick

  C House

  D Cat

GO ON

8 Read this sentence.

The ants' costumes are made by <u>securing</u> pipe cleaners on a headband.

Which word means the opposite of the word <u>securing</u>?

A Drawing

B Fastening

C Loosening

D Scratching

9 Read this sentence from the play.

Mouse comes and <u>gnaws</u> holes in me.

Which word means about the same thing as the word <u>gnaws</u>?

A Finds

B Chews

C Drills

D Stares

GO ON

10 What does Little Red Ant learn from his trip outside? Explain your answer and support it with details from the story.

_____

_____

_____

_____

_____

_____

_____

Selection Test

Tales of the Trickster

DIRECTIONS
Decide which is the best answer to each question.

1 People first made up trickster tales to —

A make listeners laugh at themselves

B explain things that happen in the world

C help people remember important events

D teach children about their family history

2 In most stories, a trickster is —

A a funny character

B a very large or very small man

C a sad character

D an animal with human features

3 How are oral stories different from written stories?

A They change over time.

B They are longer.

C They have happy endings.

D They stay the same.

4 Both Robert Greygrass and Rose Red Elk are —

A hard workers

B movie actors

C scientists

D storytellers

© Macmillan/McGraw-Hill

GO ON ➡

5 "The Ungrateful Tiger" is a trickster tale from —

(A) China

(B) India

(C) Korea

(D) Mexico

6 In American folk traditions, some trickster stories are used to —

(A) describe unusual places

(B) pass along jokes

(C) change the weather

(D) remember holidays

7 Read this sentence.

She is a <u>successful</u> storyteller herself.

The word <u>successful</u> means —

(A) filled with success

(B) before success

(C) having no success

(D) after success

GO ON

8 Read this sentence from the article.

Nowadays, scientists <u>investigate</u> and answer questions like these.

The word <u>investigate</u> means —

(A) study carefully

(B) go on an adventure

(C) invent something new

(D) have a meeting

9 Read this sentence.

Some characters in trickster tales are <u>cunning</u>.

What does the word <u>cunning</u> mean?

(A) Scared

(B) Smart

(C) Brave

(D) Unhappy

GO ON

10 Does a trickster always trick other characters? Explain your answer and support it with details from the article.

_____

_____

_____

_____

_____

_____

_____

STOP

Cook-a-Doodle-Doo!

DIRECTIONS
Decide which is the best answer to each question.

1 Which of these words best describe Rooster?

(A) Sad and lonely

(B) Lazy and selfish

(C) Nervous and foolish

(D) Patient and determined

2 Why does Rooster decide to bake a strawberry shortcake?

(A) He is going to enter a contest.

(B) He is tired of eating chicken feed every day.

(C) He wants to impress his family when they visit.

(D) He plans to teach Pig and Turtle how to bake.

3 What causes the strawberry shortcake to fall?

(A) Rooster runs to get potholders to take out the hot cake.

(B) Iguana yanks at the cake plate to bring it to the table.

(C) Pig knocks the cake over so he can taste it.

(D) Turtle reads the shortcake recipe incorrectly.

4 After they beat an egg, Iguana offers to —

(A) saw off part of a glass cup

(B) whip the cream with a stick

(C) light the stove with a lamp

(D) feed the shortcake to Pig

5 Why is the second strawberry shortcake easier to make?

    A Little Red Hen helps the animals.

    B They are no longer hungry.

    C They are now familiar with the steps.

    D Iguana takes a nap instead of helping.

6 Why does Iguana get upset with Pig?

    A Pig eats the first shortcake.

    B Pig wears a dishtowel for a hat.

    C Pig does not help with the baking.

    D Pig bothers Rooster too much.

7 Read this sentence from the story.

"That butter is just sitting there like a log," said Pig.

What does the phrase "sitting there like a log" mean?

    A Growing bark

    B Not moving

    C Floating on

    D Turning over

GO ON

8 Read this sentence.

The animals bake a <u>magnificent</u> strawberry shortcake.

The word <u>magnificent</u> means —

A beautiful and wonderful

B small but expensive

C large and very heavy

D hot and kind of flaky

9 Read this sentence from the story.

"What's our first <u>ingredient</u>?" he asked.

The word <u>ingredient</u> means something that is —

A white

B delicious

C not needed

D part of a mixture

GO ON ▶

10 How would this story be different if Rooster had made the strawberry shortcake alone? Explain your answer and support it with details from the story.

_____

_____

_____

_____

_____

_____

_____

One Riddle, One Answer

DIRECTIONS
Decide which is the best answer to each question.

1 Look at the chart below.

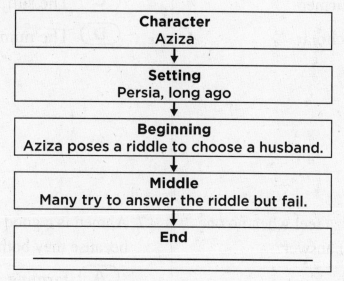

| **Character** |
| Aziza |

↓

| **Setting** |
| Persia, long ago |

↓

| **Beginning** |
| Aziza poses a riddle to choose a husband. |

↓

| **Middle** |
| Many try to answer the riddle but fail. |

↓

| **End** |
| |

Which of these belongs on the blank line?

A A farmer named Ahmed falls in love.

B The finest tutors were brought to the palace.

C Ahmed answers the riddle and marries Aziza.

D A scholar gives a good answer to the riddle.

2 What is the main problem at the beginning of this story?

A The sultan needs a teacher for Aziza.

B Aziza has a riddle to solve.

C The sultan needs an advisor.

D Aziza wants to find a husband.

3 How does Aziza choose whom to marry?

A She holds a race.

B She uses a riddle.

C She lets her father decide.

D She asks an advisor.

© Macmillan/McGraw-Hill

4 Which character thinks that a sword is the correct answer?

(A) The sultan

(B) The soldier

(C) The farmer

(D) The scholar

6 What is the answer to Aziza's riddle?

(A) Love

(B) Money

(C) The sun

(D) The number 1

5 How does Aziza feel when no one has the correct answer?

(A) Angry

(B) Excited

(C) Thankful

(D) Discouraged

7 Ahmed is a good match for Aziza because they both like —

(A) farming and horses

(B) strength and swords

(C) riddles and numbers

(D) stars and money

GO ON ▶

Selection Test

8 Read this sentence from the story.

The sultan began to seek a suitable husband for her.

Which meaning from a dictionary best fits the word suitable?

A Just right

B From far away

C Very smart

D Handsome and strong

9 Read this sentence.

Many men wanted to increase their power by marrying the sultan's daughter.

The word increase means —

A make smaller

B share

C make bigger

D hide

GO ON

10 Why did Aziza leave the palace in a caravan? Explain your answer and support it with details from the story.

_____

_____

_____

_____

_____

_____

_____

STOP

Weekly Assessment

Macmillan/McGraw-Hill

Student Name _____

Date _____

Weekly Assessment

TESTED SKILLS AND STRATEGIES

- **Reading Comprehension**
- **Vocabulary Strategies**
- **Grammar, Mechanics, and Usage**
- **Spelling**

Mc Graw Hill Macmillan/McGraw-Hill

DIRECTIONS

Read "Singing Out." Then read each question. Decide which is the best answer to each question. Mark the space for the answer you have chosen. Write your answer to question 7.

Singing Out

1   Nina Martinez shut the classroom door behind her and walked down the hall. She trudged up the steps to the second floor. She felt <u>nervous</u> this morning. Why had she decided to try out for the talent show? She loved to sing. But she <u>disliked</u> singing in front of other people.

2   Taking a deep breath, she pushed open the door of the music room and went inside. The room was filled with laughing children. There were Luz and James. There were others from her class, too. The bright, sunny room left no place to hide. A few teachers sat on folding chairs. They waited for the children to settle down. There was the stage, cold and bare.

3   "Hi, Nina!" Luz called out. "I didn't think you would try out. You are so shy."

© Macmillan/McGraw-Hill

GO ON

4   "That's nonsense," Nina said. "I'm not shy at all."

5   Luz <u>chuckled</u>. She ran off to find a seat. Nina followed, dragging her feet. She wished she were downstairs sitting at her desk. What had she gotten herself into?

6   One by one the students got up on the stage and did their acts.

7   "Nina Martinez!" a voice called out. It was Mrs. Brent, the music teacher.

8   Nina rose from her chair. She walked to the huge, empty stage. Her face was hot, and her shaking hands were as cold as ice. She fumbled with the sheet music of her favorite song, but the words would not come out.

9   "I—I—" Nina began. Then she stopped. "I can't," she said softly.

10   "Close your eyes. Pretend you are alone." said Mrs. Brent gently. "Forget about everyone else. Just sing."

11   Nina felt silly, but she gave it a try. She shut her eyes. She raised her voice and sang out. Her hands stopped shaking. The song poured out like honey from a jar.

12   Mrs. Brent clapped. "That's the first time I have really heard your voice," she said. "You are in the show!"

13   Nina gave a big sigh and smiled happily.

Page 3

1 Read the diagram below to answer the following question.

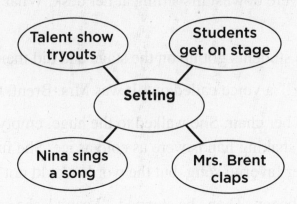

Which of these goes in the center oval?

A The music room at Nina's school

B A theater near Nina's school

C Nina's classroom in her school

D A hallway inside Nina's school

---

2 What is Nina's main problem in the story?

A She is not a very good singer.

B She is shy about singing in front of people.

C She has to wait a long time for her turn to sing.

D She is surprised to see so many children in the music room.

3 How does Nina feel when she first tries to sing?

A Brave

B Excited

C Proud

D Scared

Page 4

GO ON ▶

4 Which word means about the same as <u>nervous</u> in paragraph 1?

- Ⓐ Sleepy
- Ⓑ Certain
- Ⓒ Worried
- Ⓓ Confused

6 In paragraph 5, the word <u>chuckled</u> means —

- Ⓐ wrote a word
- Ⓑ fell
- Ⓒ walked away
- Ⓓ laughed

5 In paragraph 1, the word <u>disliked</u> means —

- Ⓐ liked before
- Ⓑ did not like
- Ⓒ liked better
- Ⓓ one who likes

7 How do Nina's feelings change by the end of the story? Explain your answer and support it with details from the story.

_____

_____

_____

_____

_____

GO ON

Page 5

DIRECTIONS

Read the introduction and the passage that follows. Then read each question and fill in the correct answer.

David wrote this story about a boy named William. He wants you to review his paper. As you read, think about the corrections and improvements that David should make. Then answer the questions that follow.

Old Friends, New Friends

(1) William did not want to move to the country. (2) He enjoyed his life in the city? (3) He would mis it a lot.

(4) He wanted to keep his friends, too. (5) He was afraid he might never see them again! (6) He would have to go to a new school where he didn't know anybody. (7) What would he do after school.

(8) When his family moved, William had good luk and made new friends quickly. (9) He stayed in touch with his old friends by email. (10) He had twice as many friends as before.

GO ON

8 What change, if any, should be made in sentence 2?

- **A** Change *He* to **She**
- **B** Change *enjoyed* to **enjoying**
- **C** Change the question mark to a period
- **D** Make no change

9 What change, if any, should be made in sentence 3?

- **A** Change *mis* to **miss**
- **B** Change *lot* to **lott**
- **C** Insert a comma after *it*
- **D** Make no change

10 What change, if any, should be made in sentence 7?

- **A** Change *What* to **When**
- **B** Change *do* to **did**
- **C** Change the period to a question mark
- **D** Make no change

11 What change, if any, should be made in sentence 8?

- **A** Change *had* to **have**
- **B** Change *luk* to **luck**
- **C** Insert a comma after *and*
- **D** Make no change

12 What change, if any, should be made in sentence 9?

- **A** Change *stayed* to **staying**
- **B** Change *with* to **which**
- **C** Change the period to a question mark
- **D** Make no change

STOP

Page 7

Student Name _____

Grade 3 • Unit 1 • Week 1
Student Evaluation Chart

Tested Skills	Number Correct	Percent Correct
Reading Comprehension: *Character, Setting, Plot, 1, 2 ,3*	/3	%
Short Answer: *Character, Setting, Plot, 7*	/3	%
Vocabulary Strategies: *Synonyms, 4; Word Parts: Prefixes, 5; Context Clues, 6*	/3	%
Grammar, Mechanics, and Usage: *Statements and Questions, 8, 10, 12*	/3	%
Spelling: *Words with Short Vowels, 9, 11*	/2	%
Total Weekly Test Score	/14	%

Weekly Assessment

Student Name _____

Date _____

Weekly Assessment

TESTED SKILLS AND STRATEGIES

- **Reading Comprehension**
- **Vocabulary Strategies**
- **Grammar, Mechanics, and Usage**
- **Spelling**

Mc Graw Hill **Macmillan/McGraw-Hill**

Read "Marta and Luis Go to Sea." Then read each question. Decide which is the best answer to each question. Mark the space for the answer you have chosen. Write your answer to question 7.

Marta and Luis Go to Sea

1   Every day, Marta and her brother Luis watched ships sail in and out of port. "Where are they going?" wondered Luis.

2   "On great adventures," sighed Marta. Secretly, she wished for an <u>adventure</u>, too.

3   "But I will miss our family!" Luis cried.

4   "Don't worry," smiled his big sister, Marta. "I'll help you. We'll get through this together! After all, you and I are family." Luis smiled for the first time in a while.

5   One day, a ship sailed in with a great hole in its side. They walked to the dock but wanted to see more of the ship. So they stepped onto the ship's deck. A deckhand let loose the lines, and the huge squares of canvas swelled up and out in the breeze.

6   "Look at the <u>fantastic</u> sails, Marta!" Luis shouted. The children gazed up at them.

GO ON ➡

Page 2

7   Then Marta saw an open hatch. "Luis! Let's see what's down there!" she whispered. The children climbed down the hatch and began <u>exploring</u>. The lower deck was piled high with supplies. They were looking with wonder at the hanging sausages, the barrels of water, and the crated chickens when they heard a sailor shout, "Cast off, mates!" They looked at each other fearfully and dashed for the ladder. Too late! Someone had slammed the hatch cover shut.

8   Marta and Luis both shouted until they were worn out, but no one heard. They soon became sleepy. Finally, they fell asleep on a pile of old sails. A few hours later, a surprised sailor found the sleeping children. He marched them to the captain.

9   "Sir," he said, "we have two stowaways." The captain listened patiently to the children's story.

10   "Well, it's too late to turn back to shore," he said, "so I will make you the cook's helpers. You both will be in charge of washing the ship's dishes." Then the captain smiled as he added, "You will also be the first children to sail the new route to India."

11   "Oh, no!" cried Luis. "What about our parents? They'll be worried about us."

12   "Don't worry! We'll let them know that you are safe," the captain said with a kind smile on his face.

13   As they followed the captain out, Luis and Marta already began feeling homesick.

14   Just then, the captain turned to the deckhand and said, "Go back to port and let the children off. I think they've learned their lesson."

15   The children looked out and realized they were just a couple of feet away from shore. As soon as they got off the ship, Luis and Marta hurried back home.

Page 3

1 Look at the chart below.

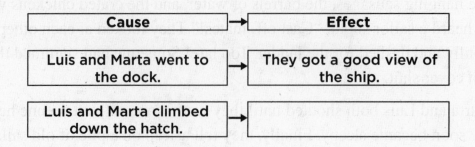

Cause	→	Effect
Luis and Marta went to the dock.	→	They got a good view of the ship.
Luis and Marta climbed down the hatch.	→	

Which of these belongs in the empty box?

- **A** The captain smiled at them.
- **B** They got trapped in the ship.
- **C** They hurried back home.
- **D** The ship went back to the port.

---

2 The children get into trouble because they are —

- **A** not careful
- **B** too trusting
- **C** too generous
- **D** not surprised

3 Where are Marta and Luis when they speak to the captain?

- **A** India
- **B** On a ship
- **C** On the dock
- **D** In their house

GO ON ▶

Page 4

Weekly Assessment

4 In paragraph 2, the word <u>adventure</u> means —

(A) long talk or discussion

(B) an older adult

(C) something bought or sold

(D) an exciting trip

5 Which meaning from a dictionary best fits the word <u>fantastic</u> in paragraph 6?

(A) At a great distance

(B) Particularly good; wonderful

(C) Made to please; fancy

(D) Existing only in one's mind

6 In paragraph 7, the word <u>exploring</u> means —

(A) looking around

(B) eating snacks

(C) climbing upward

(D) hiding quietly

7 Why did the captain tell the children they would be the cook's helpers? Explain your answer and support it with details from the story.

_____

_____

_____

_____

Page 5

GO ON ▶

DIRECTIONS
Read the introduction and the passage that follows. Then read each question and fill in the correct answer.

Josie wrote this article about a fire chief. She wants you to review her paper. As you read, think about the corrections and improvements that Josie should make. Then answer the questions that follow.

A Visit from the Fire Chief

(1) Today we had an assembly. (2) The fire chief, Chief Lopez, came to speak to us. (3) He comes to our school to talk about how to stay saife.

(4) Chief Lopez walked in and looked at us. (5) Then he yelled, "Watch out?" (6) We all jumped. (7) Then he laughed and told us we must always be alert.

(8) Chief Lopez then told us some rules to follow at hoame. (9) Never put anything over a lamp. (10) Do not cook without asking an adult?

(11) The chief also told us about the important job firefighters do. (12) These people always have to be alert and brave. (13) They move quickly when the alarm sounds.

Page 6

GO ON ➤

8 What change, if any, should be made in sentence 3?

(A) Change *comes* to **coming**

(B) Insert a comma after *school*

(C) Change *saife* to **safe**

(D) Make no change

9 What change, if any, should be made in sentence 5?

(A) Change the question mark to an exclamation point

(B) Change *yelled* to **yelling**

(C) Change *out* to **at**

(D) Make no change

10 What change, if any, should be made in sentence 8?

(A) Change *told* to **telled**

(B) Insert a comma after *rules*

(C) Change *hoame* to **home**

(D) Make no change

11 What change, if any, should be made in sentence 9?

(A) Insert **Should** before *Never*

(B) Change the period to an exclamation point

(C) Change *put* to **puts**

(D) Make no change

12 What change, if any, should be made in sentence 10?

(A) Insert **Never** before *Do*

(B) Change the question mark to a period

(C) Change *an* to **a**

(D) Make no change

Page 7

STOP

Grade 3 • Unit 1 • Week 2
Student Evaluation Chart

Tested Skills	Number Correct	Percent Correct
Reading Comprehension: *Cause and Effect, 1, 2; Character, Setting, Plot, 3*	/3	%
Short Answer: *Cause and Effect, 7*	/3	%
Vocabulary Strategies: *Context Clues, 4, 6; Dictionary: Unknown Words, 5*	/3	%
Grammar, Mechanics, and Usage: *Commands and Exclamations, 9, 11, 12*	/3	%
Spelling: *Words with Final* e *(vowel-consonant-final* e *pattern), 8, 10*	/2	%
Total Weekly Test Score	**/14**	**%**

Student Name _____

Date _____

Weekly Assessment

TESTED SKILLS AND STRATEGIES

- **Reading Comprehension**
- **Vocabulary Strategies**
- **Grammar, Mechanics, and Usage**
- **Spelling**

Macmillan/McGraw-Hill

DIRECTIONS

Read "City Gardeners." Then read each question. Decide which is the best answer to each question. Mark the space for the answer you have chosen. Write your answer to question 7.

City Gardeners

1   Open space is rare in the city, and people who live in apartments do not have lawns or land. Some people have found space for gardens. They plant them in empty lots in the city. Little pockets of green dot the cold, gray cement and make the city brighter.

© Macmillan/McGraw-Hill

2   Tomatoes, green beans, and colorful flowers grow here. Roses climb up the old brick walls. A child may play among the rows of sweet peas and squash. A jogger may sit in the sun for a while on a bench. People feel welcome in the gardens. They like to get away from the busy city streets.

3   Something special is growing in these places. It is friendship. People of all ages from the neighborhood come together in the gardens. Some people donate seeds or tools. Others contribute their time. Side by side, members of the community work to help keep their city green. As they take care of the garden, they also learn about each other. The gardeners talk and share stories. They find that they have things in common. Friendships are formed, and the friends look out for each other. That makes the streets safer for everyone.

4   Some people have other plans for the open space. They want to put up tall buildings where the gardens are planted. But they may be unaware of how important the gardens are. The gardeners do not want to give up their gardens. They want the city to stay green. The gardeners have worked hard to make something beautiful.

5   Some people are fighting to save the gardens. One way of addressing the problem is to write letters to city leaders. The letters tell why the gardens are needed. Sometimes the buildings go up anyway, but at least the gardeners try.

Page 3

GO ON ➡

1 What is this article mainly about?

(A) City gardens help build strong communities.

(B) Sometimes gardeners must stand up for their rights.

(C) Neighborhoods with city gardens are always very safe.

(D) Making new buildings is as important as planting city gardens.

2 Who owns a city garden?

(A) The builders

(B) The city leaders

(C) Everyone in the community

(D) The gardeners who work hardest

3 When people work together in a garden, they —

(A) read stories

(B) feel younger

(C) often argue

(D) become friends

4 Which word means about the same as donate in paragraph 3?

(A) Sell

(B) Give

(C) Find

(D) Lose

5 In paragraph 3, the word members means —

(A) people in a group

(B) small pockets

(C) people who own land

(D) gardening tools

6 In paragraph 4, the word unaware means —

(A) aware again

(B) very aware

(C) aware before

(D) not aware

GO ON ▶

7 How do city gardens help communities? Explain your answer and support it with details from the article.

_____

_____

_____

_____

_____

_____

_____

_____

Page 5

GO ON ➡

DIRECTIONS

Read the introduction and the passage that follows. Then read each question and fill in the correct answer.

Lina wrote this article about gardens. She wants you to review her paper. As you read, think about the corrections and improvements that Lina should make. Then answer the questions that follow.

Garden Surprise

(1) Ruben looked out the apartment window, watching the busy street below. (2) Cars and people hurried by. (3) Then noticed some people with a wheelbarrow and gardening tools. (4) One person had a paile of water. (5) Disappeared into an empty lot. (6) Ruben told his mom about it.

(7) "Let's go see what's up!" said Mom. (8) When they got to the lot, they were amazed. (9) It was a garden!

(10) "This is great!" said Ruben. (11) Ruben sat down on a bench by some flowers. (12) Chatted with the people. (13) Ruben knew they would come here often!

Page 6

GO ON ➡

8 What change, if any, should be made in sentence 3?

- **A** Insert **Ruben** after *Then*
- **B** Change *some* to **sum**
- **C** Change the period to a question mark
- **D** Make no change

9 What change, if any, should be made in sentence 4?

- **A** Change *person* to **people**
- **B** Change *had* to **have**
- **C** Change *paile* to **pail**
- **D** Make no change

10 What change should be made in sentence 5?

- **A** Change *an* to **a**
- **B** Insert **They** before *disappeared*
- **C** Change *lot* to **lott**
- **D** Insert a comma after *into*

11 What change, if any, should be made in sentence 10?

- **A** Change *This* to **These**
- **B** Change *great* to **grait**
- **C** Change *said* to **say**
- **D** Make no change

12 What is the best way to revise sentence 12?

- **A** His Mom chatted with the people.
- **B** Chatted quietly with the people.
- **C** Then him chatted with the people.
- **D** Chatted with the people some more.

STOP

Grade 3 • Unit 1 • Week 3
Student Evaluation Chart

Tested Skills	Number Correct	Percent Correct
Reading Comprehension: *Main Idea and Details, 1, 2, 3*	/3	%
Short Answer: *Main Idea and Details, 7*	/3	%
Vocabulary Strategies: *Thesaurus: Synonyms, 4; Context Clues, 5; Word Parts: Prefixes, 6*	/3	%
Grammar, Mechanics, and Usage: *Subjects, 8, 10, 12*	/3	%
Spelling: *Words with Long a (ay, ai, a_e, a, ea, ei), 9, 11*	/2	%
Total Weekly Test Score	**/14**	**%**

© Macmillan/McGraw-Hill

Student Name _____

Date _____

Weekly Assessment
TESTED SKILLS AND STRATEGIES

- **Reading Comprehension**
- **Vocabulary Strategies**
- **Grammar, Mechanics, and Usage**
- **Spelling**

Mc Graw Hill **Macmillan/McGraw-Hill**

DIRECTIONS

Read "Lone Wolf." Then read each question. Decide which is the best answer to each question. Mark the space for the answer you have chosen. Write your answer to question 7.

Lone Wolf

1   From her warm and cozy bed, Annie heard the wolf howl. She had a passion for reading, but now even she could not <u>concentrate</u> on her book. The howl was bothering her with its lonely sound. It was calling to her for help. Annie closed the book and went downstairs, where her father was looking out the window at the snow.

2   "Do you hear the wolf, Annie?" he asked.

3   "Yes! He's asking for our help, Dad. I know it," Annie said.

4   "Don't be silly," Dad said. "It must be lost. Wolves live in packs, and sometimes a hunting wolf gets lost. It howls so that the others will hear it, and then it can find its way back to its family."

© Macmillan/McGraw-Hill

GO ON ➤

5   In the morning the wolf was in the yard, and Annie and Dad watched him closely. There was something splendid about the animal. His shaggy fur was silver gray, and his eyes were yellow. Annie had to admire him. He looked so handsome. She knew he was a prince in wolf's fur! He had come to talk to her.

6   "What do wolves eat?" she asked Dad.

7   "Anything with fur," he answered. "They mostly eat wild animals."

8   Annie's heart ached for the wolf. What if he did not find his pack soon? That would be dangerous for him. Annie knew that wolves did not hunt alone—they needed the pack. Why had he asked her for help?

9   By lunchtime the wolf had disappeared, but they could still hear him howling. Then something wonderful happened. The mysterious voices of other wolves began to answer back.

10   "See? That's his family," Dad said. "He's going to find them soon. He's a lucky wolf."

11   The next day their neighbor, Mr. Nelson, came over. He said, "Say, I saw something wonderful early this morning. A pack of wolves was running along the frozen river!"

12   Annie wished she had been there. She knew the wolf prince was leading the pack, with his crown sparkling in the sun.

Page 3

1 Both Annie and her dad think that the wolf is —

- **A** scary
- **B** fun to watch
- **C** clever
- **D** easy to catch

2 Dad says that the wolf is howling because it is —

- **A** hungry
- **B** cold
- **C** afraid
- **D** lost

3 How do Annie and Mr. Nelson both feel about the wolves at the end of the story?

- **A** They think the wolves are wonderful.
- **B** They are tired of the wolves.
- **C** They think that the wolves are sick.
- **D** Their hearts ache for the wolves.

4 Which meaning of the word concentrate best fits the way it is used in paragraph 1?

- **A** Bring together
- **B** Pay attention to
- **C** Remove water from
- **D** Collect in one place

5 Which word means about the same as splendid in paragraph 5?

- **A** Grand
- **B** Lonely
- **C** Friendly
- **D** Sad

6 Which word means about the same as admire in paragraph 5?

- **A** Fear
- **B** Respect
- **C** Stare at
- **D** Make fun of

GO ON

7 How were Annie's feelings about the howling wolf different from her father's?
Explain your answer and support it with details from the story.

_____

_____

_____

_____

_____

_____

_____

Page 5

GO ON →

Read the introduction and the passage that follows. Then read each question and fill in the correct answer.

Cam wrote this story about animals. He wants you to review his paper. As you read, think about the corrections and improvements that Cam should make. Then answer the questions that follow.

The Hunt

(1) The moon high in the sky. (2) The wind began to blowe. (3) A fox barked at her mate. (4) It was time to find some dinner for their babies. (5) The two foxes out on their hunt. (6) Their eyes were as black as cole.

(7) They trotted across the field, their noses to the ground. (8) They made almost no sound as they moved. (9) Suddenly, they stopped. (10) Something was moving in the grass. (11) They sniffed the air. (12) A mouse. (13) The hunters pounced—and missed! (14) The mouse scampered away.

© Macmillan/McGraw-Hill

Page 6

8 What change, if any, should be made in sentence 1?

(A) Insert **was** after *moon*

(B) Change *high* to **hi**

(C) Change the period to a question mark

(D) Make no change

9 What change, if any, should be made in sentence 2?

(A) Change *wind* to **Wind**

(B) Change *began* to **begin**

(C) Change *blowe* to **blow**

(D) Make no change

10 What change should be made in sentence 5?

(A) Change *two* to **too**

(B) Insert **set** after *foxes*

(C) Change *foxes* to **foxs**

(D) Insert a comma after *out*

11 What change, if any, should be made in sentence 6?

(A) Change *Their* to **there**

(B) Change *were* to **was**

(C) Change *cole* to **coal**

(D) Make no change

12 What is the **BEST** way to revise sentence 12?

(A) A small mouse.

(B) Only a mouse.

(C) A mouse in the grass.

(D) It was a mouse.

STOP

Student Name _____

Grade 3 • Unit 1 • Week 4
Student Evaluation Chart

Tested Skills	Number Correct	Percent Correct
Reading Comprehension: *Compare and Contrast, 1, 3; Character, Setting, and Plot, 2*	/3	%
Short Answer: *Compare and Contrast, 7*	/3	%
Vocabulary Strategies: *Context Clues: Multiple-Meaning Words, 4; Thesaurus: Synonyms, 5, 6*	/3	%
Grammar, Mechanics, and Usage: *Predicates, 8, 10, 12*	/3	%
Spelling: *Words with Long o (o, ow, o_e, oa, oe), 9, 11*	/2	%
Total Weekly Test Score	**/14**	**%**

Weekly Assessment

Student Name _____

Date _____

Weekly Assessment

TESTED SKILLS AND STRATEGIES

- **Reading Comprehension**
- **Vocabulary Strategies**
- **Grammar, Mechanics, and Usage**
- **Spelling**

Mc Graw Hill **Macmillan/McGraw-Hill**

DIRECTIONS

Read "Closer to the Sky." Then read each question. Decide which is the best answer to each question. Mark the space for the answer you have chosen. Write your answer to question 7.

Closer to the Sky

1   David's father was an airplane pilot. He was gone for days at a time, so David's grandmother would come to David's house while his mother was at work. David often felt lonely and bored. While Grandmother cooked, she watched the birds from the window and sketched them on a pad. She could do that for hours.

2   His mom had her job, and Grandmother had her drawings. Everyone had something to do that seemed important. But David had nothing special of his own.

3   "So make something that is your own," Grandmother suggested. "What is it you would most like?" She put down her sketch pad and pencil and gave David her full attention.

4   "To be closer to the sky—and to Dad," David said. That gave him an idea. He went to the garage and found a crate once used for storage. Now it was empty. He pulled the crate apart to <u>separate</u> the boards.

5   "What are you making?" his mother asked that evening when she saw the boards.

6   "A tree house," answered David.

7   "Good idea. You can build it in the oak tree in the yard. I'll help you on Saturday." As usual, Mom had a plan.

8   Grandmother made sketches of tree houses. David picked the design he liked best. He imagined the house already built. He would go there and gaze at the sky. It would be his own special place. He could not wait to tell his father about his great idea.

9   Saturday finally came. David and his mother made exact measurements of the wood and then sawed the boards. It was hard work, but David had great determination. The most difficult part was hammering the nails into the tree trunk. David and his mother <u>ruined</u> quite a few nails, but at last the tree house was safely joined to the tree.

10   "That's a snug little house," said his grandmother. "Your father will be proud of you." Grandmother glanced over at David. "Is that a sketch pad you are holding?" she asked with a smile.

11   David climbed up to his new house, feeling like the <u>luckiest</u> boy anywhere. Sunlight dappled the leaves. There went an airplane overhead, humming like a giant bumblebee. David began to dream as he opened his sketch pad.

Page 3

1 How will David most likely feel when he sits in his tree house?

    A He will soon grow bored again.

    B He will feel lonelier than before.

    C He will no longer miss his father.

    D He will feel excited and creative.

2 If the story continued, what would David most likely do next?

    A Write a long letter to his father

    B Build some toys and games out of wood

    C Make another tree house for his grandmother

    D Sketch what he sees from the tree house

3 Why does David want to be closer to the sky?

    A He wants to grow taller.

    B His father is a pilot.

    C He likes to see the birds.

    D His mother gave him the idea.

4 In paragraph 4, the word <u>separate</u> means —

    A join together

    B break off

    C set apart

    D make even

5 What does the word <u>ruined</u> mean in paragraph 9?

    A Cut or sawed

    B Spoiled; destroyed

    C Found or made

    D Pounded; hammered

6 In paragraph 11, the word <u>luckiest</u> means —

    A most lucky

    B lucky before

    C not lucky

    D more lucky

© Macmillan/McGraw-Hill

GO ON

7 What do you think David will do the next time he has a problem? Explain
your answer and support it with details from the story.

_____

_____

_____

_____

_____

_____

_____

Page 5

GO ON ▶

DIRECTIONS

Read the introduction and the passage that follows. Then read each question and fill in the correct answer.

Steve wrote this article about making things. He wants you to review his paper. As you read, think about the corrections and improvements that Steve should make. Then answer the questions that follow.

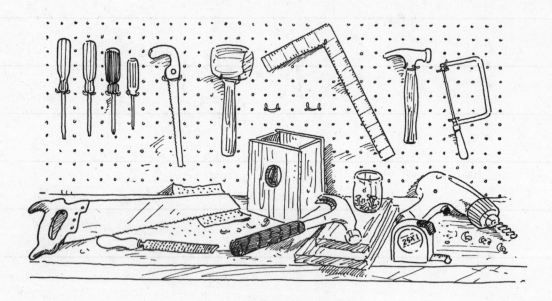

In the Shop

(1) My friend James and I like to make things. (2) We by wood and other things we need. (3) Then we work together. (4) Last week we made a birdhouse. (5) I cut the pieces of wood and he nailed them together. (6) Then we painted it brite red.

(7) Building things can be fun. (8) It can also be dangerous. (9) Remember that you can't play with tools like they are toys. (10) You should also not build with wood by yourself. (11) Ask a grownup to help you. (12) You don't want to cut your finger or hit your thumb with a hammer. (13) Follow the rules, you will be safe.

8 What change, if any, should be made in sentence 2?

- (A) Change *by* to **buy**
- (B) Insert a comma after *wood*
- (C) Change the period to a question mark
- (D) Make no change

9 What change, if any, should be made in sentence 5?

- (A) Change *I* to **me**
- (B) Insert a comma after *wood*
- (C) Change *them* to **this**
- (D) Make no change

10 What change should be made in sentence 6?

- (A) Change *we* to **us**
- (B) Change *painted* to **painting**
- (C) Change *brite* to **bright**
- (D) Change *red* to **read**

11 What is the **BEST** way to combine sentences 7 and 8?

- (A) Building things can be fun, it can also be dangerous.
- (B) Building things can be fun and it can also be dangerous.
- (C) Building things can be fun, and, can also be dangerous.
- (D) Building things can be fun, but it can also be dangerous.

12 What change, if any, should be made in sentence 13?

- (A) Insert **Don't** before *follow*
- (B) Delete the comma after *rules*
- (C) Insert **and** after the comma
- (D) Make no change

STOP

Grade 3 • Unit 1 • Week 5
Student Evaluation Chart

Tested Skills	Number Correct	Percent Correct
Reading Comprehension: *Make and Confirm Predictions, 1, 2; Cause and Effect, 3*	/3	%
Short Answer: *Make and Confirm Predictions, 7*	/3	%
Vocabulary Strategies: *Context Clues, 4, 5; Word parts: Suffixes -er, -est, 6*	/3	%
Grammar, Mechanics, and Usage: *Punctuate Compound Sentences, 9; Compound Sentences, 11, 12*	/3	%
Spelling: *Words with Long i (igh, ie, i, i_e, y), 8, 10*	/2	%
Total Weekly Test Score	/14	%

Student Name _____

Date _____

Weekly Assessment

TESTED SKILLS AND STRATEGIES

- **Reading Comprehension**
- **Vocabulary Strategies**
- **Grammar, Mechanics, and Usage**
- **Spelling**

Macmillan/McGraw-Hill

Read "Aunt Sophie's Gift." Then read each question. Decide which is the best
answer to each question. Mark the space for the answer you have chosen.
Write your answer to question 7.

Aunt Sophie's Gift

1   It was nearly Aunt Sophie's birthday, and Anya had no money for a
present. Aunt Sophie, who lived next door to Anya, said she was not
concerned about gifts, but Anya was worried. Didn't everyone love getting
presents? Maybe Aunt Sophie was a little different from most people
because she wrote poems and kept nine cats in her tiny apartment, but there
must be some present she would like. Anya thought she would go crazy
trying to think of something.

2   Mama had some suggestions: "Why don't you knit her a scarf, or bake
a cake?"

3   "There is no time to knit!" Anya wailed. "Plus, Aunt Sophie isn't fond of
sweets," she grumbled. She was getting upset, but then Anya had an idea:
she would illustrate some of her aunt's poems. Her drawing ability had

© Macmillan/McGraw-Hill

blossomed since she started taking lessons, and Anya thought she could do a fine job.

4   Anya almost skipped down the sidewalk and ran up the steps to Aunt Sophie's apartment. She knocked on the door, and her aunt came to answer. She was wearing a large scarf wrapped around her long silvery hair. She smiled at Anya. "May I copy your poems?" Anya asked Aunt Sophie.

5   "Of course you can, Anya. I'm delighted that you like them," Aunt Sophie said. She smiled and set a bowl of milk on the floor for the new kitten.

6   Anya hurried downstairs and back home and began to read. What wonderful writing! The art would have to be good, too. Anya made many sketches before she opened the tubes of colorful paints. She wanted to be sure to capture the mood of the writing. Then she carefully created a picture for each poem.

7   Finished at last, Anya bound the pages together with gold thread and made a cover, and the book was complete. How surprised Aunt Sophie would be!

8   On Friday, while Mama was cooking Aunt Sophie's favorite dinner, Anya went to get her aunt. She carried the book she made as she walked <u>upstairs</u> to her aunt's apartment. Aunt Sophie, dressed in a rainbow of colors, opened the door. A cat sat on her shoulder. The cats made sure Aunt Sophie was never lonesome.

9   Anya gave her aunt the book. "For me? Oh!" Slowly, Aunt Sophie began to turn the pages, and tears sparkled in her eyes.

Page 3

GO ON ➡

1 What happens just after Anya complains about her mother's gift suggestions?

  Ⓐ Aunt Sophie gives Anya some of her poems to copy.

  Ⓑ Anya worries about not having a gift for Aunt Sophie.

  Ⓒ Anya's mother asks her to bake a cake for Aunt Sophie.

  Ⓓ Anya gets the idea to illustrate some of her aunt's poems.

2 What does Anya do before she starts to paint?

  Ⓐ Makes sketches on paper

  Ⓑ Binds the pages of the book

  Ⓒ Shows the sketches to her aunt

  Ⓓ Knits a scarf for her aunt

3 How is Aunt Sophie different from most people?

  Ⓐ She likes presents.

  Ⓑ She has nine cats.

  Ⓒ She eats dinner.

  Ⓓ She has a birthday.

4 In paragraph 3, the word <u>wailed</u> means —

  Ⓐ slept

  Ⓑ walked

  Ⓒ laughed

  Ⓓ cried

GO ON ▶

5 Which word from paragraph 4 is a compound word?

(A) *skipped*

(B) *sidewalk*

(C) *apartment*

(D) *wrapped*

6 In paragraph 8, the word <u>upstairs</u> means —

(A) up the stairs

(B) the top floor

(C) stairs that only lead up

(D) the stairs inside an apartment

7 What steps does Anya take to make a gift for her aunt? Explain your answer and support it with details from the story.

_____

_____

_____

_____

_____

_____

_____

Page 5

GO ON ▶

DIRECTIONS

Read the introduction and the passage that follows. Then read each question and fill in the correct answer.

Theo wrote this story about a trip. He wants you to review his paper. As you read, think about the corrections and improvements that Theo should make. Then answer the questions that follow.

A Trip to Rome

(1) Mom and Dad took me to Rome last year. (2) Rome is a city in italy. (3) My parents and I had a wonderful time. (4) There were so many sights for us to see. (5) We spent a weak seeing as much as we could.

(6) We stayed in a Hotel in the middle of the city. (7) It was on a very busy street. (8) We saw beautiful fountains. (9) We also saw the ruins of ancient Rome.

(10) The food was delicious. (11) I loved the pizza. (12) I could even eat pizza for thanksgiving! (13) The Roman people eat a late lunch. (14) Then they go back to work after lunch. (15) They don't eat dinner until at least 7:30 at night.

GO ON ➤

Page 6

8 What change, if any, should be made in sentence 2?

- **A** Change *Rome* to **rome**
- **B** Change *city* to **City**
- **C** Change *italy* to **Italy**
- **D** Make no change

9 What change, if any, should be made in sentence 5?

- **A** Change *spent* to **spend**
- **B** Change *weak* to **week**
- **C** Change *seeing* to **see**
- **D** Make no change

10 What change, if any, should be made in sentence 6?

- **A** Change *stayed* to **staying**
- **B** Change *Hotel* to **hotel**
- **C** Change *middle* to **Middle**
- **D** Make no change

11 What change, if any, should be made in sentence 7?

- **A** Change *It* to **They**
- **B** Change *was* to **were**
- **C** Change *street* to **streat**
- **D** Make no change

12 What change, if any, should be made in sentence 12?

- **A** Change *I* to **Me**
- **B** Change *eat* to **ate**
- **C** Change *thanksgiving* to **Thanksgiving**
- **D** Make no change

STOP

Student Name _____

Grade 3 • Unit 2 • Week 1
Student Evaluation Chart

Tested Skills	Number Correct	Percent Correct
Reading Comprehension: *Sequence, 1, 2; Compare and Contrast, 3*	/3	%
Short Answer: *Sequence, 7*	/3	%
Vocabulary Strategies: *Context Clues, 4; Word Parts: Compound Words, 5, 6*	/3	%
Grammar, Mechanics, and Usage: *Capitalize Proper Nouns, 8; Common and Proper Nouns, 10, 12*	/3	%
Spelling: *Words with Long e (ea, ee, e_e, ie, e, ey, y), 9, 11*	/2	%
Total Weekly Test Score	/14	%

Student Name _____

Date _____

Weekly Assessment

TESTED SKILLS AND STRATEGIES

- **Reading Comprehension**
- **Vocabulary Strategies**
- **Grammar, Mechanics, and Usage**
- **Spelling**

Mc Graw Hill **Macmillan/McGraw-Hill**

Read "Family Living." Then read each question. Decide which is the best answer to each question. Mark the space for the answer you have chosen. Write your answer to question 7.

Family Living

1   Being part of a family is not always easy. There are times when members of a family do not agree.

2   Children do not always get along with their brothers and sisters. Quarreling among children is a fact of life, but sometimes there is too much fighting. The fighting begins harming the relationships that family members share, and then it is time for something to be done.

3   Children often fight over possessions. When a family is large, children want to protect what is theirs. They do not want to share a treasured toy or game. A child may become jealous of something a brother or sister purchased. Often the parents have to get involved in these arguments.

4   Sometimes a younger child wants to do what their elder siblings do. Older children usually get to try things first. Parents tell the younger child that his

GO ON

or her turn will eventually come, but the wait is sometimes too long for the child. Parents may have to let the youngster learn the lesson on his or her own to keep the younger child from being angry with the parents or being jealous of the older child.

5   When grandparents come to visit, it is usually a happy occasion. But what happens if they come to stay? Grandparents or other older relatives may come to live with a family. When this happens, it is often hard for everyone to get along at first. The grandparent is not used to living with so many people anymore, especially children. The young children are not used to having another adult in the house, and their parents have to adjust to life with their own mom or dad again. It can be stressful for everyone.

6   Living in a family can be a chore! But family members supply support and love for each other in a way that cannot be replaced. The next time you get in a fight with family members, think about how they have helped you before. Think about a time when they have beamed with happiness at a favor you did for them. Try to capture again the feeling that it gave you. The anger or hurt you feel will disappear, and you will find that being part of a family is well worth all the time and effort you have to put into it.

1 From this article, the reader can tell that remembering good times —

  A is only important for small families

  B leads to more fighting among children

  C helps family members get along better

  D is something only young children need to do

2 The reader can conclude that young children in a family —

  A need to have patience

  B will never get their turn

  C should be jealous of others

  D should fight for what they want

Page 3

GO ON ➤

3 What is paragraph 5 mostly about?

- **A** Sharing toys and games
- **B** Living with grandparents
- **C** Learning to take turns
- **D** Quarreling among children

4 Which meaning of the word supply best fits the way it is used in paragraph 6?

- **A** An amount available for use
- **B** Number of goods offered for sale
- **C** Materials needed to do something
- **D** Provide with something needed or wanted

5 In paragraph 6, the word capture means —

- **A** put in prison
- **B** hold by force
- **C** save for a long time
- **D** something that has been caught

6 In paragraph 6, the word disappear means —

- **A** feel good
- **B** become larger
- **C** go away
- **D** grow stronger

Page 4

GO ON ▶

Weekly Assessment

7 Why is having a grandparent move in with a family sometimes stressful? Explain your answer and support it with details from the article.

_____

_____

_____

_____

_____

_____

_____

Page 5

GO ON ➡

DIRECTIONS
Read the introduction and the passage that follows. Then read each question and fill in the correct answer.

Carlos wrote this story about going to the park. He wants you to review his paper. As you read, think about the corrections and improvements that Carlos should make. Then answer the questions that follow.

Looking at the Sky

(1) Kyle and his aunt like to go to the park to study the sky.
(2) She gave him an astronomy books. (3) It has information about the planets, the stars, and the moon.

(4) After school Kyle went to his aunt's houses. (5) He started to nock on the door. (6) "Will you go to the park now."

(7) His aunt laughed. (8) "Have patience, Kyle. (9) We'll go after dinner."

(10) Kyle said, "I know, but I can't wait to use my telescope. (11) The moon will be bright tonight. (12) The star will be shining, too."

(13) When dinner was over, Kyle and his aunt took his telescope to the park. (14) They had a wonderful time.

GO ON ➡

8 What change, if any, should be made in sentence 2?

  (A) Change *she* to **her**

  (B) Change *an* to **a**

  (C) Change *books* to **book**

  (D) Make no change

9 What change, if any, should be made in sentence 5?

  (A) Change *He* to **Him**

  (B) Change *nock* to **knock**

  (C) Change the period to a question mark

  (D) Make no change

10 What change, if any, should be made in sentence 6?

  (A) Change the period to a question mark

  (B) Change *Will* to **Did**

  (C) Change *park* to **parks**

  (D) Make no change

11 What change, if any, should be made in sentence 10?

  (A) Change *said* to **say**

  (B) Change *my* to **me**

  (C) Change the period to a question mark

  (D) Make no change

12 What change, if any, should be made in sentence 12?

  (A) Change *star* to **stars**

  (B) Change *shining* to **shine**

  (C) Change *too* to **two**

  (D) Make no change

STOP

Page 7

Student Name _____

Grade 3 • Unit 2 • Week 2
Student Evaluation Chart

Tested Skills	Number Correct	Percent Correct
Reading Comprehension: *Draw Conclusions, 1, 2; Main Idea and Details, 3*	/3	%
Short Answer: *Draw Conclusions, 7*	/3	%
Vocabulary Strategies: *Context Clues: Multiple-Meaning Words, 4, 5; Context Clues, 6*	/3	%
Grammar, Mechanics, and Usage: *Singular and Plural Nouns, 8, 12; Punctuate Sentences, 10*	/3	%
Spelling: *Words with Silent Letters (kn, mb, rh, gn, bu, mn, wr, gh, l), 9, 11*	/2	%
Total Weekly Test Score	**/14**	**%**

Student Name _____

Date _____

Weekly Assessment

TESTED SKILLS AND STRATEGIES

- **Reading Comprehension**
- **Vocabulary Strategies**
- **Grammar, Mechanics, and Usage**
- **Spelling**

Macmillan/McGraw-Hill

DIRECTIONS

Read " Helping Each Other." Then read each question. Decide which is the best answer to each question. Mark the space for the answer you have chosen. Write your answer to question 7.

Helping Each Other

1   Years ago, many people lived on farms. When a farmer had to build a barn, his neighbors would travel miles to go to the farm and help. This traditional event was called a barn raising. The people worked together to build the barn, watch the children, and cook enough food for a big party. Everyone worked very hard, and in one or two days a sturdy new barn would be completed. It was a lot of hard work to build a strong barn without big machines.

2   There are many reasons for people to labor so much to build another person's barn. One reason is that the people were generous and kindhearted. So if a neighbor required help, the people nearby were willing to lend a hand. The help they gave was like a gift to their neighbor. When there was hard work to be done, everyone knew it would be much <u>easier</u> with a lot of assistance.

GO ON

3   Helping a neighbor made people feel good. Also, most people try to return a favor. So a man who helped a neighbor knew he could count on that neighbor to assist him at some time in the future.

4   There was also a social aspect to a barn raising. Farm life was lonely, and miles might have separated neighbors. Building a barn brought everyone together. Old friends could chat, and young children had others their same age to run around and play with. New friendships would also be <u>established</u>, and sometimes people met their future husband or wife at a barn raising. There was usually a big party after the new barn was complete. Food and recipes were shared, music was played (often by the same men who built the barn), and people had fun.

5   Years ago, this was how many towns were built. People worked together to produce buildings that everyone used, like a schoolhouse, a courthouse, or a city hall. They also built furniture for the inside of the buildings, such as a bookcase for the schoolhouse. It was one way that people could be good neighbors, make a difference in their <u>communities</u>, and help their towns grow.

GO ON

Page 3

1 Read the chart below to answer the following question.

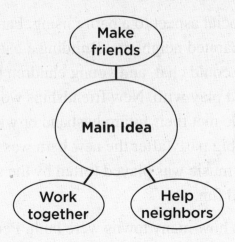

Which of these goes in the center oval?

A A man who helped a neighbor could then ask for help.

B People who built the barn also played music.

C Long ago, neighbors got together to build barns.

D There was usually a big party when the barn was done.

2 People probably helped at a barn raising because they —

A wanted someone to watch their children

B knew they would meet a future husband or wife

C wanted to produce a building for everyone to use

D knew the work would go faster with a lot of helpers

3 Which of these was a social part of a barn raising?

A Farms were often far apart.

B Young children played together.

C People tried out new equipment.

D Neighbors built furniture, too.

© Macmillan/McGraw-Hill

GO ON ➡

Page 4

4 Which word means the opposite of <u>easier</u> in paragraph 2?

(A) Harder

(B) Longer

(C) Kinder

(D) Taller

5 In paragraph 4, the word <u>established</u> means —

(A) named

(B) ended

(C) formed

(D) discussed

6 What does the word <u>communities</u> mean in paragraph 5?

(A) Places where barns could be built

(B) Groups of people with common interests

(C) Farms that raised animals and crops

(D) People who owned pieces of land

7 Why were people willing to help a neighbor build a barn? Explain your answer and support it with details from the article.

_____

_____

_____

_____

_____

_____

_____

GO ON

Page 5

DIRECTIONS

Read the introduction and the passage that follows. Then read each question and fill in the correct answer.

Emma wrote this story about a girl. She wants you to review her paper. As you read, think about the corrections and improvements that Emma should make. Then answer the questions that follow.

A Girl Named Maria

(1) Before 1974, only boys could play on Little League teams.

(2) In 1972, a girl named Maria Pepe wanted to play on a team.

(3) She could throe and catch like the boys. (4) She thought all childs should be allowed to play.

(5) The coach and players welcomed her, but others said that girls were not allowed on Little League teams. (6) Maria and her coach were upset, and they took the case to court.

(7) Years ago, many sports were played only by boys or men.

(8) But a law was passed in 1974 allowing girls to play on baseball teams. (9) News of Maria's case began to spred across the country.

(10) After that, girls and womans began playing in many new sports.

GO ON ▶

8 What change, if any, should be made in sentence 3?

- **A** Change *could* to **can**
- **B** Change *throe* to **throw**
- **C** Insert a comma after *catch*
- **D** Make no change

9 What change should be made in sentence 4?

- **A** Change *She* to **Her**
- **B** Change *thought* to **think**
- **C** Change *childs* to **children**
- **D** Change *allowed* to **allowing**

10 What change, if any, should be made in sentence 7?

- **A** Change *sports* to **sportes**
- **B** Change *were* to **was**
- **C** Change *men* to **mans**
- **D** Make no change

11 What change, if any, should be made in sentence 9?

- **A** Change *Maria's* to **Maria**
- **B** Change *began* to **beginning**
- **C** Change *spred* to **spread**
- **D** Make no change

12 What change should be made in sentence 10?

- **A** Change *womans* to **women**
- **B** Insert a comma after *womans*
- **C** Change *playing* to **play**
- **D** Change the period to a question mark

© Macmillan/McGraw-Hill

STOP

Page 7

Grade 3 • Unit 2 • Week 3
Student Evaluation Chart

Tested Skills	Number Correct	Percent Correct
Reading Comprehension: *Main Idea and Details, 1, 3; Draw Conclusions, 2*	/3	%
Short Answer: *Main Idea and Details, 7*	/3	%
Vocabulary Strategies: *Thesaurus: Antonyms, 4; Context Clues, 5, 6*	/3	%
Grammar, Mechanics, and Usage: *Irregular Plural Nouns, 9, 12; Spelling Irregular Plural Nouns, 10*	/3	%
Spelling: *Words with 3-Letter Blends (scr, str, spr, spl, thr), 8, 11*	/2	%
Total Weekly Test Score	/14	%

Weekly Assessment

Student Name _____

Date _____

Weekly Assessment

TESTED SKILLS AND STRATEGIES

- **Reading Comprehension**
- **Vocabulary Strategies**
- **Grammar, Mechanics, and Usage**
- **Spelling**

Mc Graw Hill **Macmillan/McGraw-Hill**

DIRECTIONS

Read "Making Things Better." Then read each question. Decide which is the best answer to each question. Mark the space for the answer you have chosen. Write your answer to question 7.

Making Things Better

1   On a beach just outside the town of Newport, children pick up trash. They are working in groups along with grownups. The workers sort bottles and cans into bags. Waste goes into other bags. They leave the beach much cleaner than they found it. The children talk and laugh as they do their job. The volunteers feel good about this work, which they do without pay. They are making the Newport beach look beautiful again.

2   At a nearby center, young teens are working, too. They teach younger children new skills. One volunteer shows children how to make plastic necklaces. Another teen is outside in the yard, directing a game of basketball. The young children are <u>thrilled</u> to have "big sisters" and "big brothers." Their own families are busy, but here someone has time to play with them. The children are excited about that.

© Macmillan/McGraw-Hill

Page 2

3   There is a park across town where other volunteers have gathered. They are planting flowers and pulling up weeds. They have made up a <u>slogan</u>, "Make things grow!" If you take a tour of the park, you will see children of all ages gardening. They are learning a useful skill that also helps keep the park green. The children make new friends. The adults get to know new neighbors.

4   The people who live here in Newport all agree. This area was not always such a good place for children. There were not many volunteers. Children were often bored or lonely. Few people went to the park or the beach because these places did not look very inviting.

5   Then one day a smart parent said, "Our families <u>deserve</u> a better place to live. We are responsible for making things better."

6   Volunteer groups were formed, and many people joined them. The leaders taught others what to do. When there was a job to do, people volunteered to get it done. Soon things were looking up, and people started using the park and the beach again.

1 The author probably wrote this article to —

  (A) describe the problems in one town

  (B) give information about volunteers in Newport

  (C) tell a funny story about a strange town

  (D) explain how to be a "big sister" or "big brother"

2 Why did the author describe the children's work?

  (A) To prove that children do not work hard enough

  (B) To show that children can help the community, too

  (C) To teach readers that grownups must lead the children

  (D) To warn readers that the work is too hard for most children

GO ON ▶

Page 3

3 What were volunteers doing in the park?

A Playing baseball

B Painting

C Making necklaces

D Gardening

4 Which word from the article helps the reader understand the meaning of the word <u>thrilled</u> in paragraph 2?

A *nearby*

B *outside*

C *excited*

D *families*

5 In paragraph 3, the word <u>slogan</u> means —

A sign

B friendly greeting

C command

D memorable phrase

6 In paragraph 5, the word <u>deserve</u> means —

A have earned

B see through

C know about

D write on

GO ON

7 Why did the author describe the town before and after the volunteers started working? Explain your answer and support it with details from the article.

_____

_____

_____

_____

_____

_____

_____

GO ON ➡

DIRECTIONS

Read the introduction and the passage that follows. Then read each question and fill in the correct answer.

Dan wrote this story about his friend Kia. He wants you to review his paper. As you read, think about the corrections and improvements that Dan should make. Then answer the questions that follow.

Kia Volunteers

(1) Last week, Kia's teacher told the class about a group of volunteers. (2) She said they meet every month at the park. (3) Kia asked what kind of projects they did.

(4) "They do so mutch," the teacher replied. (5) "For example, they clean up areas. (6) They fix elderly peoples houses and build benches in parks."

(7) Kia thought about her teachers answer. (8) She wanted to pich in and help.

(9) The next day, the group came to Kia's school. (10) "Who would like to work with us?" they asked. (11) Kia raised her hand right away.

Page 6

GO ON ➡

Weekly Assessment

8 What change, if any, should be made in sentence 1?

(A) Change *Kia's* to **Kias**

(B) Change *told* to **tell**

(C) Change *teacher* to **teecher**

(D) Make no change

9 What change, if any, should be made in sentence 4?

(A) Change *They* to **Them**

(B) Change *do* to **does**

(C) Change *mutch* to **much**

(D) Make no change

10 What change, if any, should be made in sentence 6?

(A) Change *peoples* to **people's**

(B) Change *benches* to **benchs**

(C) Insert a comma after *houses*

(D) Make no change

11 What change, if any, should be made in sentence 7?

(A) Change *Kia* to **Kia's**

(B) Change *her* to **his**

(C) Change *teachers* to **teacher's**

(D) Make no change

12 What change, if any, should be made in sentence 8?

(A) Change *wanted* to **wanting**

(B) Change *pich* to **pitch**

(C) Change the period to a question mark

(D) Make no change

STOP

Page 7

Grade 3 • Unit 2 • Week 4
Student Evaluation Chart

Tested Skills	Number Correct	Percent Correct
Reading Comprehension: *Author's Purpose, 1, 2; Main Idea and Details, 3*	/3	%
Short Answer: *Author's Purpose, 7*	/3	%
Vocabulary Strategies: *Context Clues, 4, 5, 6*	/3	%
Grammar, Mechanics, and Usage: *Possessive Nouns, 8, 11; Apostrophes in Possessive Nouns, 10*	/3	%
Spelling: *Words with Digraphs (consonant digraphs th, ch, tch, sh, wh, ng, ph), 9, 12*	/2	%
Total Weekly Test Score	/14	%

Student Name _____

Date _____

Weekly Assessment

TESTED SKILLS AND STRATEGIES

- **Reading Comprehension**
- **Vocabulary Strategies**
- **Grammar, Mechanics, and Usage**
- **Spelling**

Macmillan/McGraw-Hill

DIRECTIONS

Read "Good Neighbors." Then read each question. Decide which is the best answer to each question. Mark the space for the answer you have chosen. Write your answer to question 7.

Good Neighbors

1   Mr. and Mrs. Winter had lived in the yellow house on the corner since my family had moved here from Florida. They told us that they had been in that house for over 50 years. Dad said the Winters were once lively people who raked leaves, shoveled snowy sidewalks, and chatted with everyone who passed by. But lately nobody had seen much of Mr. or Mrs. Winters. We were beginning to get worried about them.

2   So one chilly day in February, Dad paid the older couple a visit. When he returned, he looked concerned. I heard him tell Mom, "Their roof is leaky, and most of their kitchen appliances need to be repaired. I'm going to take a crew over there tomorrow and get some things done."

3   Dad works in construction and knows how to do building repairs. Construction work is pretty slow during the cold months, so he's had some time on his hands. It is just like him to want to help others, too.

GO ON

Weekly Assessment

4   "Good idea, Luis," Mom agreed. "I left the Winters a plate of cookies last week, but I never thought to look around the place, and they would never complain to me."

5   "I'd like to help, too," I said. "I could work after school." My parents quickly agreed after I promised to get home in time to do my homework. I was looking forward to it.

6   Bright and early the next day, Dad went downtown to get his <u>equipment</u>. He came back with a small crew, and they got right to work. After school I went over to the Winters' house, and Dad and Ravi showed me how to patch the kitchen floor with new tiles. Will and Jesse were up on the roof fixing the leak. Greg, a whiz with machinery, had already found out what was wrong with the stove and was fitting the new parts. Everyone was happy to help.

7   Mr. Winter could not stop thanking everyone, and Mrs. Winter made plates of sandwiches for the crew. "I'd love to cook a hot meal," she said. "When the stove is mended, I'll do just that. You'll all come for dinner, won't you?" Her green eyes sparkled as she said, "This is about the best thing that has happened in a long time."

8   You know, I felt the same way.

Page 3

GO ON

1 Read the chart below and answer the question that follows.

The Winters need some help.

↓

Mom leaves cookies for them.

↓

Dad takes a crew to the house.

↓

Theme

Which idea belongs in the last box?

A. Always ask others for help.

B. Good neighbors help each other.

C. Good neighbors are hard to find.

D. People work better if they are rewarded.

2 Which would be another good title for this story?

A. "Fixing a House"

B. "Lending a Hand"

C. "The New House"

D. "Luis's Busy Day"

3 Why does Dad have time to help the Winters?

A. His work is slow during the cold months.

B. He has just moved in from Florida.

C. He lost his job a few weeks ago.

D. Mrs. Winters asks him over for dinner.

GO ON ▶

4 In paragraph 2, the word appliances means —

(A) gifts

(B) foods

(C) machines

(D) crews

5 Which word in paragraph 3 helps the reader understand the meaning of construction?

(A) *months*

(B) *slow*

(C) *building*

(D) *cold*

6 In paragraph 6, the word equipment means —

(A) tools

(B) workers

(C) books

(D) sandwiches

7 What is the theme, or message, of this story? Explain your answer and support it with details from the story.

_____

_____

_____

_____

_____

Page 5

GO ON ➡

DIRECTIONS

Read the introduction and the passage that follows. Then read each question and fill in the correct answer.

Jason wrote this article about teddy bears. He wants you to review his paper. As you read, think about the corrections and improvements that Jason should make. Then answer the questions that follow.

The Teddy Bear

(1) Picture books are good gifts for children. (2) Teddy bears are good gifts for children, too. (3) Do you know how the teddy bear got its name? (4) It wasnt named for a place. (5) It was actually named after a president.

(6) President Teddy Roosevelt once saved the life of a baby bear. (7) A candy maker named Morris Michtom saw a funny picture of this. (8) It gave him the idea to make a few stuffed bears for his friends. (9) He called them "Teddy's bears." (10) This story was told in a book, The teddy bear.

(11) Before long, many people wanted stuffed bears. (12) Soon Mr. Michtom was making candy. (13) He was also making teddy bears. (14) He didnt sell much candy, but he sold a lot of bears.

© Macmillan/McGraw-Hill

Page 6

GO ON ▶

8 What is the **BEST** way to combine sentences 1 and 2?

(A) Picture books are good gifts, and teddy bears are good gifts.

(B) Picture books are good gifts for children and teddy bears.

(C) Picture books for children are good gifts for teddy bears.

(D) Picture books and teddy bears are good gifts for children.

9 What change, if any, should be made in sentence 4?

(A) Change *It* to **Them**

(B) Change *wasnt* to **wasn't**

(C) Change *named* to **names**

(D) Make no change

10 What change, if any, should be made in sentence 10?

(A) Change *This* to **These**

(B) Change *was* to **were**

(C) Change *The teddy bear* to The Teddy Bear

(D) Make no change

11 What is the **BEST** way to combine sentences 12 and 13?

(A) Soon Mr. Michtom was making candy and teddy bears.

(B) Soon Mr. Michtom was making candy, and he was making teddy bears.

(C) Soon Mr. Michtom was making candy, making teddy bears, too.

(D) Soon Mr. Michtom was also making candy, but teddy bears, too.

12 What change, if any, should be made in sentence 14?

(A) Change *He* to **Him**

(B) Change *didnt* to **didn't**

(C) Change *bears* to **beares**

(D) Make no change

STOP

Page 7

Grade 3 • Unit 2 • Week 5
Student Evaluation Chart

Tested Skills	Number Correct	Percent Correct
Reading Comprehension: *Theme, 1, 2; Cause and Effect, 3*	/3	%
Short Answer: *Theme, 7*	/3	%
Vocabulary Strategies: *Context Clues, 4, 5, 6*	/3	%
Grammar, Mechanics, and Usage: *Sentence Combining with Nouns, 8, 11 Book Titles, 10*	/3	%
Spelling: *Contractions (I've, she's, aren't, weren't), 9, 12*	/2	%
Total Weekly Test Score	**/14**	**%**

Student Name _____

Date _____

Weekly Assessment

TESTED SKILLS AND STRATEGIES

- **Reading Comprehension**
- **Vocabulary Strategies**
- **Grammar, Mechanics, and Usage**
- **Spelling**

DIRECTIONS

Read "Astrid Lindgren, Writer." Then read each question. Decide which is the best answer to each question. Mark the space for the answer you have chosen. Write your answer to question 7.

Astrid Lindgren, Writer

1   Do you know Pippi Longstocking? She lives with a horse and a monkey. She is the strongest girl on Earth. Pippi takes her friends on adventures, and she is very funny. She makes the best pancakes.

2   There are many stories about Pippi. The Pippi books have been made into movies, too. The girl with red hair is famous. Readers have long loved this fun character.

3   Astrid Lindgren was a gifted author. She wrote the Pippi stories. When this <u>talented</u> author was young, she liked to read books about strong girls. Lindgren thought stories about "<u>proper</u>" children were dull because the characters always behave in the correct way. She wanted to write books about real children instead. Lindgren wrote the very first Pippi book for her own daughter. Karin Lindgren loved the book. It was a big success. So her mother wrote more Pippi books. Each book has an exciting new tale to tell.

4   Lindgren went on to write many books for children. None of her characters is boring! She put fun into her books. She got some of her ideas

© Macmillan/McGraw-Hill

GO ON

from old folk tales. In these tales, children leave home early and set out to learn about the world. Along the way they meet different people. They also learn about themselves. That is just what Lindgren's characters do. The stories teach readers lessons about themselves and about life.

5   Some people thought Lindgren's books were *too* exciting. "Why can't she write about good children?" they asked.

6   But Lindgren had other ideas. She felt that excitement was missing from children's books. She knew that being a child is special. Childhood is when you explore life for the first time.

7   Lindgren once talked about her writing. She said she wanted to help children understand others. In the world of Lindgren's books, all kinds of people find acceptance. They learn about others, and they win approval for themselves. These are useful lessons.

8   Pippi Longstocking is not always polite. But she teaches us how to live. She tries something new every single day. She makes mistakes, but she learns from them. And Pippi makes friends wherever she goes. Most importantly, Pippi loves life and adventure, and she always has a good time.

1 Astrid Lindgren wrote children's stories because she wanted to —

   A teach children manners

   B help children enjoy reading

   C inform readers about her daughter

   D persuade readers to go on adventures

2 Why did the author of the article write paragraph 3?

   A To teach the reader how to write

   B To entertain the reader with a story

   C To show how Lindgren got started as an author

   D To convince the reader that Pippi is a fun character

GO ON ▶

3 The article says that Lindgren got some of her story ideas from —

   A old folktales

   B her friends

   C Pippi Longstocking

   D her daughter Karin

4 Which word in paragraph 3 helps the reader understand what the word talented means?

   A *author*

   B *gifted*

   C *young*

   D *strong*

5 Which word in paragraph 3 helps the reader understand the meaning of proper?

   A *behave*

   B *correct*

   C *strong*

   D *children*

6 Which word in paragraph 7 helps the reader understand the meaning of acceptance?

   A *talked*

   B *writing*

   C *world*

   D *approval*

GO ON ➡

Page 4

7 Why did the author write "Astrid Lindgren, Writer"? Explain your answer and support it with details from the article.

_____

_____

_____

_____

_____

_____

_____

_____

Page 5

GO ON ➡

DIRECTIONS
Read the introduction and the passage that follows. Then read each question and fill in the correct answer.

Justine wrote this article about reading. She wants you to review her paper. As you read, think about the corrections and improvements that Justine should make. Then answer the questions that follow.

Reading

(1) Whenever I have some free time, I like to read. (2) I also like to lern about new things. (3) I read all kinds of books and magazines. (4) I read letters from my pen pal, too. (5) His name is Josh, and he lives in Amarillo Texas.

(6) My favorite author is Astrid Lindgren. (7) She writes the funniest books. (8) Her stories take place in many parts of the world, too. (9) Last month I read Pippi in the South Seas. (10) Pippi goes to visit her father. (11) He is the ruler of an island. (12) What adventures they have!

(13) Sometimes I read mysteries. (14) My brother, Jake, and I share them. (15) We try to figure out the mystery before the end of the book. (16) Usually, he gets the mystery before I do.

GO ON ➡

8 What change, if any, should be made in sentence 2?

    A Change *I* to **Me**

    B Insert a comma after *like*

    C Change *lern* to **learn**

    D Make no change

9 What change, if any, should be made in sentence 5?

    A Change the period to an exclamation point

    B Change *lives* to **live**

    C Insert a comma after **Amarillo**

    D Make no change

10 What change, if any, should be made in sentence 8?

    A Change *stories* to **storys**

    B Insert a comma after *place*

    C Change *world* to **wurld**

    D Make no change

11 What is the **BEST** way to revise sentence 11?

    A He rules an island.

    B He is the ruler of a island.

    C Of an island he is the ruler.

    D He is the ruler, of an island.

12 What is the **BEST** way to revise sentence 16?

    A He gets the mystery before I do usually.

    B Usually, he solves the mystery before I do.

    C Before I do, usually, he gets the mystery.

    D He gets the mystery before I usually do.

STOP

Grade 3 • Unit 3 • Week 1
Student Evaluation Chart

Tested Skills	Number Correct	Percent Correct
Reading Comprehension: *Draw conclusions, 1; Author's Purpose, 2; Main Idea and Details, 3*	/3	%
Short Answer: *Author's Purpose, 7*	/3	%
Vocabulary Strategies: *Context Clues, 4, 5, 6*	/3	%
Grammar, Mechanics, and Usage: *Commas in Dates, Places, and Addresses, 9; Action Verbs, 11, 12*	/3	%
Spelling: *Words with r-Controlled Vowels er, ir, ur, 8, 10*	/2	%
Total Weekly Test Score	**/14**	**%**

Student Name _____

Date _____

Weekly Assessment

TESTED SKILLS AND STRATEGIES

- **Reading Comprehension**
- **Vocabulary Strategies**
- **Grammar, Mechanics, and Usage**
- **Spelling**

Macmillan/McGraw-Hill

Read "Going Away." Then read each question. Decide which is the best answer to each question. Mark the space for the answer you have chosen. Write your answer to question 7.

Going Away

1   Roberto stood by the gate and waited for his grandpa to find the ticket and his passport. People hurried this way and that in the crowded airport. It was Roberto's first time in an airport. Never before had he been on a plane. It took many hours to fly from Italy to the United States, and Grandpa would not be coming with him. How quickly life could change!

2   "My boy," Grandpa said gently, "you will enjoy life in California. You'll make so many new friends. How delighted your father will be to have you with him again!"

3   "I do not want to leave you!" cried Roberto. "Look at this airport! I will get lost without you. That is what will happen to me in California." He hated the airport. Everyone here seemed unhappy. All around him were mothers

© Macmillan/McGraw-Hill

GO ON ➡

with crying babies in their arms. People were rushing around with faces that were tight with worry. Roberto thought of the brown cows on the farm back home and of the white chickens that scratched in the earth. This morning Roberto had eaten his last egg from those chickens and his last pear from the old tree in the yard.

4   The <u>crackle</u> of a speaker above them made Roberto jump at the sharp sound. A voice from the loud speaker <u>announced</u> that it was time to board the plane. Grandpa squeezed Roberto tightly. He said, "Go. When you are unhappy, look in this envelope."

5   The plane <u>soared</u> into the sky and flew away. Roberto glanced at the starry sky as the world grew dark. He opened the envelope as he wiped away a tear. Inside was a photograph of a smiling Grandpa. His hat was pushed back on his head. There was his old stone house, too. Roberto smiled. He would write his grandpa a letter as soon as he arrived at his new home.

---

1 Read the chart below to answer the question that follows.

Plot	Setting
Roberto says goodbye to Grandpa.	

Which of these goes in the empty box?

(**A**) On a farm

(**B**) On a plane

(**C**) In an airport

(**D**) In California

Page 3

2 What is Roberto's main problem in the story?

   A He is afraid to fly in an airplane.

   B He does not really know his father.

   C He does not want to change schools.

   D He is leaving Italy and will miss his grandfather.

3 What does Roberto do as the plane flies away?

   A Opens the envelope

   B Makes new friends

   C Pushes his hat back

   D Gives Grandpa a hug

4 What words in paragraph 4 help the reader understand the meaning of the word crackle?

   A *a speaker*

   B *above them*

   C *sharp sound*

   D *Roberto jump*

5 In paragraph 4, the word announced means —

   A made known

   B saw through

   C wondered aloud

   D whispered quietly

6 What words in paragraph 5 help the reader understand the meaning of the word soared?

   A *the sky*

   B *flew away*

   C *The plane*

   D *grew dark*

GO ON

© Macmillan/McGraw-Hill

7 How does Roberto feel in this story, and why? Explain your answer and
support it with details from the story.

_____

_____

_____

_____

_____

_____

_____

DIRECTIONS

Read the introduction and the passage that follows. Then read each question and fill in the correct answer.

Ali wrote a story about a girl. She wants you to review her paper. As you read, think about the corrections and improvements that Ali should make. Then answer the questions that follow.

Moving

(1) Maya's house looks like it has been hit by a tornado. (2) There are boxes everywhere. (3) That is because the Colon family is moving from El Paso to Fort Worth. (4) It is a big move. (5) Maya's parents is excited, but Maya does not want to leave. (6) She will miss her friends.

(7) "I do not want to move," Maya says. (8) She packed some more of her clothes. (9) Then she holds up her red soccer shortes. (10) "Who will play soccer with me?"

(11) Her father walking into the room. (12) "Maya," he says, "this is a good move for the whole family. (13) I have a great new job. (14) And our new home has a nice, big yard. (15) It will be great for soccer."

Page 6

GO ON

8 What change, if any, should be made in sentence 5?

　A Change *Maya's* to **Mayas**

　B Change *is* to **are**

　C Change *want* to **wants**

　D Make no change

9 What change, if any, should be made in sentence 8?

　A Change the period to an exclamation point

　B Change *She* to **Her**

　C Change *packed* to **packs**

　D Make no change

10 What change, if any, should be made in sentence 9?

　A Change *holds* to **holding**

　B Insert a comma after *red*

　C Change *shortes* to **shorts**

　D Make no change

11 What change, if any, should be made in sentence 11?

　A Change *father* to **Father**

　B Change *walking* to **walks**

　C Change the period to a question mark

　D Make no change

12 What change, if any, should be made in sentence 14?

　A Change *our* to **are**

　B Change *has* to **have**

　C Change *yard* to **yarde**

　D Make no change

STOP

Grade 3 • Unit 3 • Week 2
Student Evaluation Chart

Tested Skills	Number Correct	Percent Correct
Reading Comprehension: *Character, Setting, Plot, 1, 2, 3*	/3	%
Short Answer: *Character, Setting, Plot, 7*	/3	%
Vocabulary Strategies: Context *Clues, 4, 5, 6*	/3	%
Grammar, Mechanics, and Usage: *Subject-Verb Agreement, 8; Present-Tense Verbs, 9, 11*	/3	%
Spelling: *Words with r-Controlled Vowels ar, or, 10, 12*	/2	%
Total Weekly Test Score	/14	%

Student Name _____

Date _____

Weekly Assessment

TESTED SKILLS AND STRATEGIES

- **Reading Comprehension**
- **Vocabulary Strategies**
- **Grammar, Mechanics, and Usage**
- **Spelling**

Macmillan/McGraw-Hill

DIRECTIONS

Read "Computers Then and Now." Then read each question. Decide which is the best answer to each question. Mark the space for the answer you have chosen. Write your answer to question 7.

Computers Then and Now

1   You probably know how to use computers. You may have used one at home, at school, or at the library. But who first built these objects? One of the very first was Kenneth H. Olsen. He started by fixing radios in his basement. Later Olsen went to a famous college to learn about building machines.

2   Olsen was very good at his work. Soon he showed people how to build a computer. This machine was not meant for entertainment. It was a tool for gathering information. Olsen started his own company to make computers.

3   Who knew computers would become so important? Bill Gates did! He made some smart predictions. He and his friend Paul Allen worked together. They created a computer program that many people could use. They formed their own company. It was a great success, and Bill Gates now holds the record as the world's richest man. Most computers today use this company's programs. If you have used a computer, you have probably used these programs.

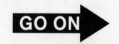

Page 2

4   Steve Jobs also loved computers. He wanted to find a way to make them cost less. That way, more people could buy them. He and his friend Steve Wozniak started a computer company. It made computers that were easy to use. The company also made a computer mouse that people liked. Today Jobs's and Wozniak's machines are sold everywhere.

5   Michael Dell was born to sell things. He did not build computers. He decided to <u>focus</u> on selling them for less money. His company sells computers directly to people. This saves people money. They do not have to buy computers at a store. Today many schools use computers sold by Dell's famous company.

6   All of these men have brought computers to many people. Experts <u>estimate</u> that more than one billion personal computers are in use today. Computers help people work and gather information. They are used in many other things, too, such as video games and cell phones. These things might not even look like computers, but they are. Computers have changed the way people live. It is difficult to imagine life today without computers.

1 Kenneth Olsen started his own company to —

  A teach people

  B make computers

  C sell machines

  D provide entertainment

2 Why did Steve Jobs want to make computers that cost less?

  A He worked with Steve Wozniak.

  B They would be easier to use.

  C People would like the mouse.

  D More people could buy them.

Page 3

GO ON

3 Bill Gates and Paul Allen started a company to make —

(A) computer programs

(B) cell phones

(C) entertainment centers

(D) adding machines

4 Which meaning of <u>record</u> best fits the way it is used in paragraph 3?

(A) An account in writing

(B) To set down for future use

(C) A performance that is better than all others of its kind

(D) To put on tape, CD, disk, or the like for later playback

5 In paragraph 5, the word <u>focus</u> means —

(A) spend money

(B) fix or concentrate

(C) provide help

(D) change or revise

6 In paragraph 6, the word <u>estimate</u> means —

(A) change the price

(B) call by telephone or radio

(C) hold a contest

(D) make a judgment or guess

Page 4

GO ON

7 Why is it hard to imagine life without computers? Explain your answer and support it with details from the article.

_____

_____

_____

_____

_____

_____

_____

Page 5

GO ON

DIRECTIONS

Read the introduction and the passage that follows. Then read each question and fill in the correct answer.

Dean wrote this article about an art school. He wants you to review his paper. As you read, think about the corrections and improvements that Dean should make. Then answer the questions that follow.

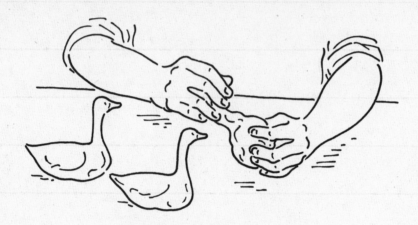

New Art School Opens

(1) A new art school has come to town. (2) It opens last week in the mall. (3) Two women run the school. (4) There are classes for children and adults. (5) Classes include painting jewelry making, and pottery.

(6) The teachers encourage students to create their own projects. (7) One pottery student is making a complete model of a farm. (8) Yesterday she makes a barn and two cows.

(9) Other students bring in unwanted junk from home. (10) They use the "junk" to make art. (11) The teachers say this is a good way to recykle things.

(12) "Everyone should take this class," said one student. (13) "It's a lot of fun."

Page 6

GO ON ➡

8 What change, if any, should be made in sentence 2?

- **(A)** Change *It* to **She**
- **(B)** Change *opens* to **opened**
- **(C)** Change *week* to **weak**
- **(D)** Make no change

9 What change, if any, should be made in sentence 5?

- **(A)** Change the period to a question mark
- **(B)** Change *Classes* to **Class's**
- **(C)** Insert a comma after *painting*
- **(D)** Make no change

10 What change, if any, should be made in sentence 8?

- **(A)** Change *she* to **her**
- **(B)** Change *makes* to **made**
- **(C)** Change *cows* to **cowes**
- **(D)** Make no change

11 What change, if any, should be made in sentence 9?

- **(A)** Change *Others* to **Other**
- **(B)** Change *unwanted* to **unwaunted**
- **(C)** Insert a comma after *junk*
- **(D)** Make no change

12 What change, if any, should be made in sentence 11?

- **(A)** Change *teachers* to **teacheres**
- **(B)** Change *say* to **saying**
- **(C)** Change *recykle* to **recycle**
- **(D)** Make no change

STOP

Page 7

Grade 3 • Unit 3 • Week 3
Student Evaluation Chart

Tested Skills	Number Correct	Percent Correct
Reading Comprehension: *Cause and Effect*, 1, 2, 3	/3	%
Short Answer: *Cause and Effect*, 7	/3	%
Vocabulary Strategies: *Homographs, 4; Context Clues, 5, 6*	/3	%
Grammar, Mechanics, and Usage: *Past-Tense Verbs, 8, 10; Commas in a Series, 9*	/3	%
Spelling: *Words with Prefixes (re-, un-, pre-, mis-, dis-)*, 11, 12	/2	%
Total Weekly Test Score	**/14**	**%**

Student Name _____

Date _____

Weekly Assessment

TESTED SKILLS AND STRATEGIES

- **Reading Comprehension**
- **Vocabulary Strategies**
- **Grammar, Mechanics, and Usage**
- **Spelling**

Mc Graw Hill Macmillan/McGraw-Hill

DIRECTIONS

Read "The Silk Road." Then read each question. Decide which is the best answer to each question. Mark the space for the answer you have chosen. Write your answer to question 7.

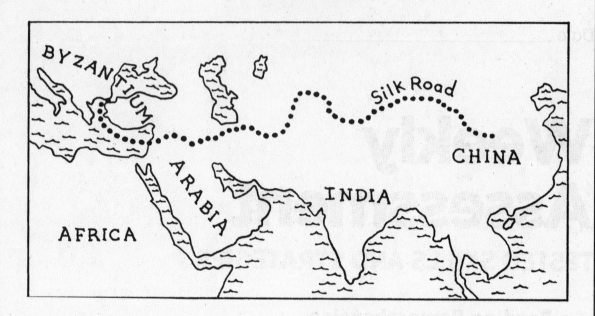

The Silk Road

1   Long ago, traders brought silk, spices, and other treasures from the East to the West. They followed the Silk Road. This passed through China, Turkey, and Greece. From there the goods were brought to Western Europe.

2   Because there were no paved roads or sidewalks, traders had a rough trip through the lonesome lands. The camels and horses that pulled the loads had to be strong. First, traders had to cross over a desert. Then they crossed over a high mountain range. Once over the mountains, the traders had many hundreds of miles to go before finally reaching Europe.

3   There were many dangers along the way. Robbers, for <u>instance</u>, roamed the land. The robbers knew that the goods the traders carried were worth a fortune. Bad weather was also a danger and could slow the traders down.

4   The Silk Road was not one particular road. There were many ways to travel from the East to the West, and each route led to different trading

© Macmillan/McGraw-Hill

GO ON

Page 2

posts. While some traders traveled by land, some merchants traveled by sea to reach the shores of Europe. Sea crossings also had their dangers. Pirates and storms were always threats. It was a hard way to make a living, but over many years trade blossomed between the East and the West.

5   Valuable silk from China was something everyone wanted. Making it was hard work. Silk comes from the cocoon of the silkworm. The silkworms had to be tended while they spun the silk threads. Then the silk threads had to be woven into fine material with soft textures. The feel of silk is slick and soft, and this <u>texture</u> makes it popular.

6   Traders were not allowed to take silkworms out of China. The money made from the silk trade was very important to China's people. They could not let other people find ways to make silk, because then people might not buy it from China.

7   Over the centuries, many changes came about because of trade on the Silk Road. People learned about new customs, beliefs, and styles of living in other parts of the world. Travelers carried stories about faraway lands. They brought back <u>sketches</u> to illustrate what they had seen. They ate new spices and wore different clothes. Trade made the world seem smaller.

GO ON

Page 3

1 Read the chart below to answer the question that follows.

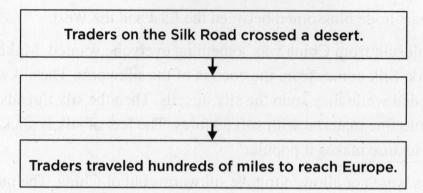

Traders on the Silk Road crossed a desert.

↓

↓

Traders traveled hundreds of miles to reach Europe.

Which of these goes in the empty box?

A Traders had a rough trip.

B Camels and horses had to be strong.

C Traders crossed over a high mountain range.

D Some traders traveled by sea to reach Europe.

2 According to the article and the map, where did the traders start out on the Silk Road?

A China

B Turkey

C Europe

D Greece

3 What did the silk makers have to do first?

A Find a way to carry the silk to the West

B Weave the silk threads into fine material

C Make sure other people did not get the silkworms

D Take care of the worms while they spun silk threads

Page 4

GO ON ▶

4 In paragraph 3, the word <u>instance</u> means —

(**A**) fortune

(**B**) danger

(**C**) goods

(**D**) example

5 Which words in paragraph 5 help the reader understand the meaning of <u>texture</u>?

(**A**) *Valuable silk*

(**B**) *slick and soft*

(**C**) *hard work*

(**D**) *makes it popular*

6 Which words in paragraph 7 help the reader understand the meaning of <u>sketches</u>?

(**A**) *to illustrate*

(**B**) *new spices*

(**C**) *different clothes*

(**D**) *seem smaller*

7 What changes came about because of trade on the Silk Road? Explain your answer and support it with details from the article.

_____

_____

_____

_____

_____

_____

© Macmillan/McGraw-Hill

GO ON

DIRECTIONS

Read the introduction and the passage that follows. Then read each question and fill in the correct answer.

Chelsea wrote this story about a trip. She wants you to review her paper. As you read, think about the corrections and improvements that Chelsea should make. Then answer the questions that follow.

My Trip

(1) My family and I are getting ready for a big trip. (2) In April, we will visit our friends in Miami, Florida. (3) As soon as we get there, we went to the beach. (4) We will visit some museums, too. (5) If we have time, we visit Key Largo.

(6) Florida was my first choyce for vacation. (7) I said, let's go to Miami.

(8) I love Miami. (9) We'll have fun with our friends. (10) We'll eat boiled lobster and clams. (11) We'll go deep-sea fishing. (12) It will be great.

© Macmillan/McGraw-Hill

Page 6

GO ON ▶

8 What change, if any, should be made in sentence 3?

    (A) Change *we* to **us**

    (B) Change *there* to **their**

    (C) Change *went* to **will go**

    (D) Make no change

9 What change, if any, should be made in sentence 5?

    (A) Change *have* to **has**

    (B) Insert **will** before *visit*

    (C) Change *Key Largo* to **key largo**

    (D) Make no change

10 What change, if any, should be made in sentence 6?

    (A) Change *first* to **furst**

    (B) Insert a comma after *Florida*

    (C) Change *choyce* to **choice**

    (D) Make no change

11 What is the **BEST** way to revise sentence 7?

    (A) I said, Let's go to Miami.

    (B) I said: Let's go to Miami.

    (C) I said, "Let's go to Miami."

    (D) "I said, Let's go to Miami."

12 What change, if any, should be made in sentence 10?

    (A) Change *We'll* to **We're**

    (B) Change *boiled* to **boyled**

    (C) Change the period to a question mark

    (D) Make no change

STOP

Grade 3 • Unit 3 • Week 4
Student Evaluation Chart

Tested Skills	Number Correct	Percent Correct
Reading Comprehension: *Sequence* 1, 3; *Main Idea and Details*, 2	/3	%
Short Answer: *Sequence*, 7	/3	%
Vocabulary Strategies: *Context Clues*, 4, 5, 6	/3	%
Grammar, Mechanics, and Usage: *Future-Tense Verbs*, 8, 9, 11	/3	%
Spelling: *Words with Diphthong /oi/ (oi, oy)*, 10, 12	/2	%
Total Weekly Test Score	**/14**	**%**

© Macmillan/McGraw-Hill

Student Name _____

Date _____

Weekly Assessment

TESTED SKILLS AND STRATEGIES

- **Reading Comprehension**
- **Vocabulary Strategies**
- **Grammar, Mechanics, and Usage**
- **Spelling**

Mc Graw Hill **Macmillan/McGraw-Hill**

DIRECTIONS

Read "At a Coral Reef." Then read each question. Decide which is the best answer to each question. Mark the space for the answer you have chosen. Write your answer to question 7.

At a Coral Reef

1   It would be Jeff's first time swimming at a coral reef. He was so excited! This year, he was going on a trip to Puerto Rico with his uncle Tito. The trip would have been too expensive for Jeff's family. But Uncle Tito travels all over the world, and he invited Jeff on this trip for free.

2   On the plane, Jeff could not sit still. He kept walking up and down the aisle. Finally, the flight attendant asked him politely to sit down. Back in his seat, Jeff thought about his family. He wanted to remember every detail of this trip. "I'll tell them all about it when I get home," he thought.

3   The next morning, Jeff and Uncle Tito swam to a coral reef. Jeff was surprised at how warm the water was. He lived in Maine. There, the ocean was almost always cold. He never went swimming in winter. He thought it was like that everywhere. But it was February, and here in Puerto Rico the water was warm!

Page 2

GO ON ➡

4   It was hard to believe this was all real. Jeff had never seen so many brightly colored fish in one place. And the coral was just as pretty. In some places it was even more colorful than the fish. Jeff thought the reef must be the most beautiful place in the world. He knew he was seeing something really special.

5   Before the trip, Jeff had read books about coral. He learned that most coral is brittle. Rough waves can break it. Jeff knew there were certain things that he was not supposed to do. Jeff knew never to stand on coral because that could hurt it. He learned never to take live coral out of the water. That can kill it. He also learned that he should never touch living coral. He could get hurt touching it.

6   Jeff was glad he had learned about coral before coming to Puerto Rico. Now he would not make an <u>innocent</u> mistake that might hurt the coral or hurt him. He could spend all of his time enjoying the fish and the reef.

---

1 The reader can tell from clues in the story that coral is —

(A) very delicate

(B) all the same color

(C) used for many things

(D) found only in cold water

2 When he is on the plane, Jeff feels —

(A) worried

(B) embarrassed

(C) excited

(D) unhappy

GO ON

Page 3

3 How is the ocean near Maine different from the ocean near Puerto Rico?

(A) It has brightly colored fish.

(B) It is much colder.

(C) It has beautiful coral reefs.

(D) It is good for swimming.

4 Which word means the same as <u>expensive</u> in paragraph 1?

(A) Costly

(B) Difficult

(C) Pretty

(D) Long

5 Which word from the story is pronounced the same as <u>aisle</u> in paragraph 2?

(A) *all*

(B) *almost*

(C) *detail*

(D) *I'll*

6 In paragraph 6, the word <u>innocent</u> means —

(A) causing damage or injury

(B) hard to understand

(C) free from guilt or blame

(D) planned ahead of time

7 What kind of person is Jeff? Explain your answer and support it with details from the story.

_____

_____

_____

_____

_____

_____

_____

Page 5

GO ON ▶

Read the introduction and the passage that follows. Then read each question and fill in the correct answer.

Raul wrote this article about an art show. He wants you to review his paper. As you read, think about the corrections and improvements that Raul should make. Then answer the questions that follow.

Art Show Coming Soon

(1) The Jordan School Art Show will be held next Thursday night at 7:00. (2) The school is located on Main Street in Bishop Texas. (3) All students and their families are invited.

(4) Our students paint pictures. (5) Our students make pottery. (6) Now they have entered their works in the show. (7) Come and look at these wonderful pieces of art!

(8) The third graders are serving drinks. (9) The third graders are selling snacks. (10) You will find them under the red and bloue sign in the lunchroom.

(11) At 8:00, Mr. Bronson, the art teacher, will announce the winners of the art contest. (12) Who will be the winners? (13) You will find out soon!

Page 6

GO ON ➡

8 What change, if any, should be made in sentence 2?

   A Change *is* to **are**

   B Insert a comma after *Bishop*

   C Change the period to an exclamation point

   D Make no change

9 What is the **BEST** way to combine sentences 4 and 5?

   A Our students paint pictures and make pottery.

   B Our student paint pictures, our students make pottery.

   C Our students paint pictures, they make pottery.

   D Our students paint and make pictures and pottery.

10 What change, if any, should be made in sentence 7?

   A Change *look* to **looke**

   B Insert a comma after *wonderful*

   C Change the exclamation point to a question mark

   D Make no change

11 What is the **BEST** way to combine sentences 8 and 9?

   A The third graders are serving drinks, they are selling snacks.

   B The third graders are serving drinks, and the third graders are selling snacks.

   C The third graders are serving drinks and selling snacks.

   D The third graders are serving and selling drinks and snacks.

12 What change, if any, should be made in sentence 10?

   A Change *will find* to **found**

   B Change *bloue* to **blue**

   C Insert a comma after *sign*

   D Make no change

STOP

Student Name _____

Grade 3 • Unit 3 • Week 5
Student Evaluation Chart

Tested Skills	Number Correct	Percent Correct
Reading Comprehension: *Make Inferences, 1, 2; Compare and Contrast, 3*	/3	%
Short Answer: *Make Inferences, 7*	/3	%
Vocabulary Strategies: *Synonyms, 4; Dictionary: Homophones, 5; Context Clues, 6*	/3	%
Grammar, Mechanics, and Usage: *Commas and Punctuation, 8; Sentence Combining with Verbs, 9, 11*	/3	%
Spelling: *Words with Variant Vowels /ü/ and /u̇/ (oo, ou, u_e, ue, ew, ui, ou), 10, 12*	/2	%
Total Weekly Test Score	**/14**	**%**

© Macmillan/McGraw-Hill

Student Name _____

Date _____

Weekly Assessment
TESTED SKILLS AND STRATEGIES

- **Reading Comprehension**
- **Vocabulary Strategies**
- **Grammar, Mechanics, and Usage**
- **Spelling**

Mc Graw Hill Macmillan/McGraw-Hill

Caterpillar Week

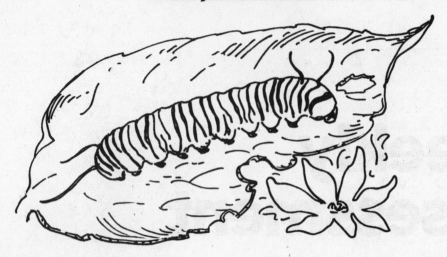

1   Cory woke up early that first morning at Aunt Kate's house. The birds were making a racket with their quarreling outside his window, and he could not sleep while they argued. Cory went outside, where his aunt was in the potting shed cutting some pieces from a plant with an old pair of shears—one of her most treasured possessions.

2   "What's that?" Cory asked her. He pointed to the plant she was cutting.

3   "Good morning! This is milkweed—that's what my caterpillars eat," she replied.

4   "Why do you raise caterpillars?" Cory asked.

5   Raising caterpillars was a hobby for his aunt.

6   "I enjoy it, and there are fewer butterflies and open areas for milkweed plants than there used to be. City life seems to be harming them, so by raising butterflies and the plants they eat, we can help protect these insects. It's a very exciting hobby!"

7   Cory looked around the potting shed and could not see what was so exciting. He examined a group of black and green caterpillars that were

© Macmillan/McGraw-Hill

GO ON ➡

consuming the milkweed leaves. "What else do they eat?" he asked. The white sap oozing from the leaf did not look tasty to him.

8   "Nothing. Monarch caterpillars eat only milkweed. I purchased the seeds and raised the plants, so now I have a supply of caterpillar food," Aunt Kate said.

9   Then Cory spotted some greenish-blue capsules in one plastic enclosure. "What are those things?" Cory wanted to know.

10   "Those are the chrysalises," said Aunt Kate. "Each caterpillar makes a sticky liquid that dries to become a shell. The shell is called a chrysalis, and inside that shell a transformation takes place. The caterpillar changes, turning into its adult form. In a few days, we'll see what emerges from these."

11   That week Cory took part in all kinds of butterfly farming activities. He helped his aunt feed the caterpillars, and he watched the chrysalises. He enjoyed getting involved in butterfly farming.

12   One morning his aunt woke him, saying, "Today is the day."

13   They hurried to the potting shed, where something amazing was happening. The chrysalises were breaking open! Out of each struggled an orange and black butterfly with its wings folded together. The butterflies crawled to the sticks in the enclosure and hung there until their wings were dry.

14   "They are on their way!" Aunt Kate exclaimed. Cory saw her <u>beam</u> with happiness.

15   Cory looked at their beautiful wings and thought that raising butterflies was a pretty exciting hobby after all.

GO ON

Page 3

1 From this story, the reader can tell that Cory —

  A is visiting Aunt Kate for a week

  B has always lived with Aunt Kate

  C has seen Aunt Kate's butterflies before

  D sent Aunt Kate her first butterflies as a present

2 What is the most likely reason city life is not good for the butterflies?

  A The traffic and noise frighten the insects.

  B There is too little room for the insects to fly.

  C Many city people catch the butterflies for pets.

  D There are few places for milkweed to grow.

3 How can the reader tell that Aunt Kate is a good gardener?

  A She likes to raise butterflies.

  B She uses old shears to cut pieces from a plant.

  C She knows that monarchs eat milkweed.

  D She grows milkweed from seeds.

4 In paragraph 1, the word quarreling means —

  A flying

  B arguing

  C going

  D digging

Page 4

GO ON ➡

Weekly Assessment

5 In paragraph 1, what does the word possessions mean?

- (A) Places where people live
- (B) People who help others
- (C) Hobbies that a person enjoys
- (D) Things that belong to someone

6 Which meaning of the word <u>beam</u> is used in paragraph 14?

- (A) Shine brightly
- (B) A long piece of wood
- (C) Give a big smile
- (D) A ray of light

7 What clues from the story show that Cory's feelings about his aunt's hobby change during the week? Explain your answer and support it with details from the story.

_____

_____

_____

_____

_____

_____

GO ON

Page 5

Read the introduction and the passage that follows. Then read each question and fill in the correct answer.

Ellie wrote this story about a man in a balloon. She wants you to review her story. As you read, think about the corrections and improvements that Ellie should make. Then answer the questions that follow.

Balloon Ride

(1) On a beautiful spring day, a croud gathers to watch a man with a balloon. (2) The man uses a special machine to fill his balloon with hot air. (3) The balloon gets bigger and bigger until it is completely full. (4) Now the man be ready to take off. (5) The balloon rises with a little bownce, and then it leaves the ground. (6) The man have a big smile on his face as he waves to the people below. (7) The man in the balloon seems to want the people to wave back, and so they do. (8) Soon the balloon is too far away to see.

© Macmillan/McGraw-Hill

8 What change, if any, should be made in sentence 1?

   A Change *croud* to **crowd**

   B Change *gathers* to **gathering**

   C Change the period to a question mark

   D Make no change

9 What change, if any, should be made in sentence 4?

   A Insert a comma after *man*

   B Change *be* to **is**

   C Change *to* to **too**

   D Make no change

10 What change, if any, should be made in sentence 5?

   A Change *rises* to **rise**

   B Change *bownce* to **bounce**

   C Take out the comma before *and*

   D Make no change

11 What change, if any, should be made in sentence 6?

   A Change *have* to **has**

   B Change *he* to **him**

   C Change *waves* to **wave**

   D Make no change

12 What change, if any, should be made in sentence 7?

   A Change *people* to **peoples**

   B Take out the comma after *back*

   C Change *do* to **does**

   D Make no change

STOP

Page 7

Grade 3 • Unit 4 • Week 1
Student Evaluation Chart

Tested Skills	Number Correct	Percent Correct
Reading Comprehension: *Draw Conclusions, 1, 2, 3*	/3	%
Short Answer: *Draw Conclusions, 7*	/3	%
Vocabulary Strategies: *Context Clues, 4, 5; Context Clues: Multiple-Meaning Words, 6*	/3	%
Grammar, Mechanics, and Usage: *Verbs: be, do, have, 9; Subject-Verb Agreement, 11, 12*	/3	%
Spelling: *Words with Diphthong ou, ow, 8, 10*	/2	%
Total Weekly Test Score	/14	%

Student Name _____

Date _____

Weekly Assessment

TESTED SKILLS AND STRATEGIES

- **Reading Comprehension**
- **Vocabulary Strategies**
- **Grammar, Mechanics, and Usage**
- **Spelling**

Mc Graw Hill Macmillan/McGraw-Hill

DIRECTIONS

Read "Old Pictures." Then read each question. Decide which is the best answer to each question. Mark the space for the answer you have chosen. Write your answer to question 7.

Old Pictures

1   Sam sat at the table, leafing through Grandma's family album. The photographs were faded, and some were cracked with age.

2   "Who is this?" Sam said, pointing.

3   "That's my father, and his name was Sam, too," Grandma answered, smiling at some faraway image Sam could not see. All he saw was a small man in an odd-looking hat and a dark suit that looked too big.

4   "You wouldn't think so by glancing at him, but my father was a great hero," Grandma said with <u>affection</u>.

5   "I thought he worked in a newspaper office," Sam remembered.

6   "He did, when he came to the United States," Grandma said. "That was after the family fled Russia."

7   "Why did they leave Russia?" Sam wondered.

8   "A terrible war was starting," she said. "Some people didn't want to believe it, but your great-grandpa sensed the danger. His brothers and sisters

© Macmillan/McGraw-Hill

did not want to go at first, so he <u>pleaded</u>. They listened to him because he was the oldest. He had very little money, but he knew that the family had to escape to France, and from there to the United States."

9   "So how did he manage that?" Sam asked.

10   "He made his <u>preparations</u> quickly. He sold everything the family owned to purchase train tickets. They quietly slipped out of town before dawn. There were also some people who did not want families to escape, but somehow Grandpa and his family got to France. It was a very unhappy time," Grandma said, and she shuddered as if she were numb with cold.

11   "Why did you shake like that, Grandma?" Sam asked as he embraced his grandmother.

12   "Your great-grandpa later found out that a week after the family's flight, fighting started and many people were killed," she replied.

13   "He got his brothers and sisters out of there just in time," Sam said as he realized what had happened. "This picture of the whole family together is very special."

14   "It is, Sam. It's a special picture," Grandma said.

15   The little man in the old photo seemed bigger now in Sam's eyes.

GO ON ➡

Page 3

1 What is one important idea in this story?

A Kids often look like their grandparents.

B Not all stories are true.

C The past can be interesting.

D It is fun to visit new countries.

2 What does Sam learn about heroes?

A They all fought in wars.

B They never run away.

C They are very tall.

D They don't always look special.

3 Why did Grandpa leave Russia?

A He knew that a war was coming.

B He had no family there.

C He did not speak the language.

D He wanted to work for a newspaper.

4 Which word from a thesaurus is a synonym for affection in paragraph 4?

A Love

B Surprise

C Anger

D Excitement

Page 4

GO ON

5 In paragraph 8, the word <u>pleaded</u>
means —

- **(A)** listened
- **(B)** wondered
- **(C)** begged
- **(D)** thought

6 What does the word <u>preparations</u>
mean in paragraph 10?

- **(A)** Tools that are needed for a project
- **(B)** Things someone does to get ready
- **(C)** People who travel often
- **(D)** Instructions for a job to be done

7 How does this story show that ordinary people can do brave things? Explain your answer and support it with details from the story.

_____

_____

_____

_____

_____

_____

_____

GO ON ➤

DIRECTIONS

Read the introduction and the passage that follows. Then read each question and fill in the correct answer.

Mark wrote this report about wild animals. He wants you to review his report. As you read, think about the corrections and improvements that Mark should make. Then answer the questions that follow.

Our New Neighbors

(1) It used to be that to see certain animals, you had to travel to the country. (2) These days, lots of wild animals are showing up in citys and suburbs. (3) They are learning how to survive around people.

(4) White-tailed deer everywhere. (5) They are beautiful, but they cause lots of damage to gardens. (6) They are also a danger to drivers.

(7) Foxs are also moving into many neighborhoods. (8) These beautiful animals live on mice and squirrels?

(9) Even coyotes are coming to town. (10) Now many people wake up at night to the sound of coyotes howling.

GO ON ➡

8 What change, if any, should be made in sentence 2?

(**A**) Change *days* to **Days**

(**B**) Change *are* to **is**

(**C**) Change *citys* to **cities**

(**D**) Make no change

9 What is the **BEST** way to revise sentence 4?

(**A**) So many white-tailed deer everywhere.

(**B**) The white-tailed deer everywhere.

(**C**) White-tailed deer everywhere!

(**D**) White-tailed deer are everywhere.

10 What change, if any, should be made in sentence 7?

(**A**) Change *Foxs* to **Foxes**

(**B**) Change *are* to **is**

(**C**) Change *neighborhoods* to **neighborhood's**

(**D**) Make no change

11 What change, if any, should be made in sentence 8?

(**A**) Change *live* to **lives**

(**B**) Change *animals* to **animales**

(**C**) Change the question mark to a period

(**D**) Make no change

12 What change, if any, should be made in sentence 9?

(**A**) Change *coyotes* to **coyote**

(**B**) Change *are* to **is**

(**C**) Insert an exclamation mark after *town*

(**D**) Make no change

STOP

Page 7

Grade 3 • Unit 4 • Week 2
Student Evaluation Chart

Tested Skills	Number Correct	Percent Correct
Reading Comprehension: *Theme, 1, 2; Plot, 3*	/3	%
Short Answer: *Theme, 7*	/3	%
Vocabulary Strategies: *Thesaurus: Synonyms, 4; Context Clues, 5, 6*	/3	%
Grammar, Mechanics, and Usage: *Linking Verbs, 9; End Punctuation and Complete Sentences, 11, 12*	/3	%
Spelling: *Plurals, 8, 10*	/2	%
Total Weekly Test Score	**/14**	%

Student Name _____

Date _____

Weekly Assessment

TESTED SKILLS AND STRATEGIES

- **Reading Comprehension**
- **Vocabulary Strategies**
- **Grammar, Mechanics, and Usage**
- **Spelling**

Mc Graw Hill **Macmillan/McGraw-Hill**

DIRECTIONS

Read "Does It Belong Here?" Then read each question. Decide which is the best answer to each question. Mark the space for the answer you have chosen. Write your answer to question 7.

Does It Belong Here?

This type of daisy grows all over the easten United States, but it is native to Europe and Asia.

1   It is fun to walk through a garden blooming with beautiful flowers and plants. But did you know that one of the biggest problems in a garden can be the plants and flowers themselves? That is because some plants are not native to the area where they are planted. *Native* means being born in a certain place. Non-native plants might be just fine inside the garden, but if they begin to sprout outside the garden they can spread and become a huge problem.

2   How do these plants begin to grow where no one planted them? Often non-native seeds are carried on the wind. These seeds can also spread on windless days. People can go for a walk in the garden and pick up non-native seeds on their shoes or clothing. When they walk around outside the garden, the seeds fall into the soil. The seeds begin to grow, and soon there is a new plant in the neighborhood. One way to solve this problem is to

GO ON

check your shoes and clothes for seeds after spending time in the garden. You can also change your clothes after gardening.

3   Often, the new plant keeps spreading. It begins to take space away from the native plants. It also uses all the water that native plants need to live. Non-native plants have taken over entire fields this way. A field with native plants and flowers will have a lot of animal life. Birds and insects feed on the plants. In a field that has been taken over by a non-native plant, there may not be very many animals. The native animals need native plants to eat. In some places, people have ripped up fields of non-native plants and replanted native plants. Then the native animals return.

4   All over the world, there is growing awareness that non-native plants can cause serious problems. Experts emphasize that we must control these plants. One solution is never to plant non-native plants in the first place. Utilize native plants in your garden instead. You will be doing a big favor to the native plants and animals in your neighborhood.

1 Read the diagram below to answer the question that follows.

Non-native plants grow where no one planted them.
↓
People walk through gardens and pick up seeds on their clothes.
↓
People work in gardens and pick up seeds on their clothes.
↓
People carry seeds without knowing it.
↓
Solution

Which of these goes in the *Solution* box?

A People should not wear shoes in the garden.

B People should not be allowed to have gardens.

C People should not go out when it's windy.

D People should change their clothes after gardening.

---

2 What is the problem when non-native plants take over fields?

A There is no water.

B There are no flowers.

C Native animals disappear.

D Non-native seeds disappear.

3 What does the word <u>windless</u> mean in paragraph 2?

A With no wind

B Full of wind

C Like the wind

D Windy again

GO ON ➤

Page 4

4 Which word means about the same as <u>awareness</u> in paragraph 4?

- **A** Excitement
- **B** Trouble
- **C** Trust
- **D** Knowledge

5 In paragraph 4, the word <u>utilize</u> means —

- **A** look for
- **B** use
- **C** sell
- **D** pick

6 How can people best solve the problem of non-native plants taking over fields?

- **A** Rip them up and replant native plants.
- **B** Pour lots of water on the fields.
- **C** Bring more native animals to the fields.
- **D** Plant native seeds among the non-native plants.

7 How can the reader help solve the problem of spreading non-native plants? Explain your answer and support it with details from the article.

_____

_____

_____

_____

_____

_____

Page 5

GO ON ▶

DIRECTIONS

Read the introduction and the passage that follows. Then read each question and fill in the correct answer.

Olivia wrote this report about butterflies. She wants you to review her report. As you read, think about the corrections and improvements that Olivia should make. Then answer the questions that follow.

Endangered Butterflies

(1) Our class is studying endangered butterflies. (2) Last week, we had a visit from a butterfly expert. (3) "Butterflies are in danger for several reasons," the expert said. (4) "Chemicals you can put on your laun are harming them," Ms. Frank explained. (5) "The trees they live in are being cut down." (6) She said there arent as many blue butterflies as there used to be in California. (7) Monarch butterflies wont survive if their favorite food, milkweed, disappears. (8) Finally, the expert taught us ways that we can help save butterflies. (9) Saving them isn't always difficult. (10) I plan to plant some of the butterfly's favorite flowers in my yard.

Page 6

GO ON

8 What change, if any, should be made in sentence 4?

   A Change *laun* to **lawn**

   B Change *Ms. Frank* to **Ms. frank**

   C Change the period to a question mark

   D Make no change

9 What change, if any, should be made in sentence 6?

   A Change *She* to **Her**

   B Change *arent* to **aren't**

   C Change *butterflies* to **butterflys**

   D Make no change

10 What change, if any, should be made in sentence 7?

   A Change *wont* to **won't**

   B Change *survive* to **survives**

   C Change *their* to **there**

   D Make no change

11 What change, if any, should be made in sentence 8?

   A Change *taught* to **taut**

   B Insert a comma after *ways*

   C Change the period to an exclamation mark

   D Make no change

12 What change, if any, should be made in sentence 9?

   A Change *Saving* to **Save**

   B Change *them* to **it**

   C Change *isn't* to **isnt**

   D Make no change

STOP

Grade 3 • Unit 4 • Week 3
Student Evaluation Chart

Tested Skills	Number Correct	Percent Correct
Reading Comprehension: *Problem and Solution, 1, 2, 6*	/3	%
Short answer: *Problem and Solution, 7*	/3	%
Vocabulary Strategies: *Word Parts: Suffixes -less, -ful, -ly, 3; Synonyms, 4; Context Clues, 5*	/3	%
Grammar, Mechanics, and Usage: *Contractions with Not 9; Spelling Contractions with Not, 10, 12*	/3	%
Spelling: *Words with Variant Vowels au, aw, alt, alk, all, ough, 8, 11*	/2	%
Total Weekly Test Score	**/14**	**%**

Student Name _____

Date _____

Weekly Assessment

TESTED SKILLS AND STRATEGIES

- **Reading Comprehension**
- **Vocabulary Strategies**
- **Grammar, Mechanics, and Usage**
- **Spelling**

DIRECTIONS

Read "My Baby Brother." Then read each question. Decide which is the best answer to each question. Mark the space for the answer you have chosen. Write your answer to question 7.

My Baby Brother

1   I was in my room the day they brought Timothy home from the hospital. I didn't feel like getting out of bed to see anyone. I heard their voices as they came into the house and decided to call out for my mom.

2   "I don't feel good!"

3   I knew if I said that, she would come running upstairs and make me feel better.

4   I especially did not want to go downstairs because I didn't want to see Timothy. He was just a strange-looking little person. I had seen him the day before in the hospital, and <u>unfortunately</u>, I was not thrilled.

5   "Mom!" I called again from bed. Where was she? She usually came right away when I needed her. Maybe she forgot about me now that she had Timothy. Was I going to have to <u>pretend</u> that I was sick?

GO ON

6   Suddenly, I heard my dad's feet on the stairs.

7   "Jason," he said, "can you come down and give me a hand? I need your help removing Mom's things from the car."

8   Mom had gotten a lot of gifts and flowers when she was in the hospital. Now Dad was asking for my help with that stuff.

9   "I don't feel like it," I told him. "I need Mom to come up."

10   "She cannot come upstairs right now because she is tired and needs a rest. She is on the couch with Timothy, waiting for you to say hello."

11   I just said, "I can't."

12   "Jason, you're going to have to get used to someone else needing Mom sometimes. Now please come downstairs. I need your help."

13   Dad sounded tired and <u>cross</u>, but so was I. I knew I should help him, though. I went downstairs, hoping I could sneak past Timothy.

14   That's when I saw them. Mom was sitting on the couch with her head back and her eyes closed. She looked very tired. I sat down next to her and gave her a hug. I wanted to make her feel better.

15   "Mom?" I said softly. "Are you okay?"

16   She smiled then. It was a beautiful, warm smile. "I'm fine, sweetie. And look who I brought home to see you." She held out a little, warm bundle in a blanket. She pulled the blanket down a little so I could see his face.

17   And, you know, he looked just like me. I started smiling, and I could swear he smiled right back at me. Then I softly touched his hand. Timothy grabbed my finger and held it tightly in his tiny palm. He liked me. Maybe having a baby brother wasn't going to be that bad.

Page 3

GO ON ▶

1 What is Jason's biggest problem in this story?

(A) He doesn't feel well.

(B) He has to carry a lot of stuff.

(C) He is upset about his baby brother.

(D) He is alone in the house.

2 What problem does Jason's dad have?

(A) He doesn't know where Jason is.

(B) He has to unpack the car.

(C) He is feeling sick and tired.

(D) He can't find Mom's things.

3 Dad gets Jason out of his room by —

(A) asking for his help

(B) saying he will punish him

(C) showing him his baby brother

(D) having Jason's mom call him

4 What is the meaning of <u>unfortunately</u> in paragraph 4?

(A) A person who is lucky

(B) In a way that is not lucky

(C) Lucky again

(D) More lucky

© Macmillan/McGraw-Hill

Page 4

GO ON ➤

5 In paragraph 5, the word
   pretend means —

   (A) act like

   (B) hide

   (C) remember

   (D) wonder if

6 What does the word cross mean
   in paragraph 13?

   (A) Confused

   (B) Happy

   (C) Grumpy

   (D) Excited

7 How does seeing the baby help solve Jason's problem? Explain your answer
   and support it with details from the story.

   _____

   _____

   _____

   _____

   _____

   _____

   _____

Page 5

GO ON ▶

Philip wrote this report about pollution in our water. He wants you to review his report. As you read, think about the corrections and improvements that Philip should make. Then answer the questions that follow.

Pollution in Our Water

(1) Living things need fresh air and water. (2) Scientists test the amount of waste in our air, water, and soil to see if there healthy. (3) The government passes laws to protect Earth from harm. (4) Yet some people feel that much more should be done.

(5) On Tuesday, my friends and I talking about how we can help to protect Earth. (6) Jean said, Let's get some samples of water from the pond behind the school."

(7) "Yes, said Christopher, "then we can have it tested for pollution."

(8) I made the point that if we find pollution, its our responsibility to write a letter to the state government.

GO ON ➡

© Macmillan/McGraw-Hill

8 What change, if any, should be made in sentence 2?

    (A) Change *test* to **tests**

    (B) Take out the comma after *air*

    (C) Change *there* to **they're**

    (D) Make no change

9 What change, if any, should be made in sentence 5?

    (A) Change *Tuesday* to **tuesday**

    (B) Change *talking* to **were talking**

    (C) Insert a comma after *talking*

    (D) Make no change

10 What change, if any, should be made in sentence 6?

    (A) Insert quotation marks before *Let's*

    (B) Change *Let's* to **Lets**

    (C) Take out the quotation marks after *school*

    (D) Make no change

11 What change, if any, should be made in sentence 7?

    (A) Add quotation marks after *Yes,*

    (B) Change *can have* to **can having**

    (C) Change the period to a question mark

    (D) Make no change

12 What change, if any, should be made in sentence 8?

    (A) Change *made* to **maked**

    (B) Change *its* to **it's**

    (C) Put quotation marks around the sentence

    (D) Make no change

Page 7

STOP

Grade 3 • Unit 4 • Week 4
Student Evaluation Chart

Tested Skills	Number Correct	Percent Correct
Reading Comprehension: *Problem and Solution, 1, 2, 3*	/3	%
Short Answer: *Problem and Solution, 7*	/3	%
Vocabulary Strategies: *Word Parts: Prefixes re-, un-, mis-, pre-, 4; Context Clues, 5, 6*	/3	%
Grammar, Mechanics, and Usage: *Main and Helping Verbs, 9; Quotation Marks in Dialogue, 10, 11*	/3	%
Spelling: *Homophones, 8, 12*	/2	%
Total Weekly Test Score	**/14**	**%**

Student Name _____

Date _____

Weekly Assessment

TESTED SKILLS AND STRATEGIES

- **Reading Comprehension**
- **Vocabulary Strategies**
- **Grammar, Mechanics, and Usage**
- **Spelling**

DIRECTIONS

Read "Mysterious Mars." Then read each question. Decide which is the best answer to each question. Mark the space for the answer you have chosen. Write your answer to question 7.

Mysterious Mars

1   People have always been curious about Mars. After all, it is fairly close to Earth. Mars is one of the inner planets, or the planets closest to the sun. It is the fourth planet from the sun in our solar system and is easily seen with a telescope. But what else do we know about it?

2   The inner planets are alike in some ways. Like Earth, Venus, and Mercury, Mars is made of rock. Like Earth, it has valleys, hills, and plains. Other farther planets, such as Jupiter, are made of gas. Nothing can live on a planet made of gas.

3   For years people have studied Mars to see if there is life on the planet. Scientists report signs of water, and most experts agree that there was probably water on Mars at one time. Water is essential for all living things. Without it, plants cannot grow and animals cannot exist. The main areas of Mars look like dry stream beds. Water may be hidden under the planet's ice caps.

4   The temperatures on Mars are very cold. That would make life as we know it difficult on Mars. Large dust storms sweep the surface and may last

GO ON

© Macmillan/McGraw-Hill

for many months. They can cover the whole planet and dim the sunlight. It would be hard to breathe or see in such a bad dust storm.

5   NASA has been exploring Mars for over 30 years. First, in 1975, *Viking* was sent to Mars. The spacecraft had two parts: an orbiter and a lander. When *Viking* got near Mars, the lander separated from the orbiter. Next, it landed. It was the first spacecraft to land safely on Mars. It took photographs to look for signs of life.

6   Then *Pathfinder* traveled to Mars in 1996. First, it entered the planet's atmosphere. Second, it used parachutes to slow its descent. Finally, it used giant air bags to cushion its landing. After landing, it sent more than 16,000 images back to the scientists on Earth! Specialists studied the pictures. They decided that although Mars is dry today, it was probably wet long ago.

7   Next, *Mars Polar Lander* went to Mars in 1999. Its job was to look for water under the planet's south ice cap. Sadly, it was lost before it could do any research.

8   Finally, two robots named *Spirit* and *Opportunity* were sent to Mars. The robots landed safely in 2004. Since then they have traveled for miles across the planet. They have taken photographs and picked up soil. They have collected lots of evidence about this mysterious planet.

1 Read the diagram below to answer the following question.

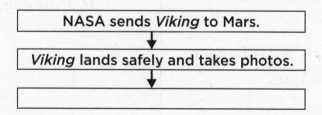

Which of these goes in the empty box?

A Scientists visit Mars to look for water.

B Temperatures on Mars are very cold.

C NASA sends *Pathfinder* to Mars.

D Two robots land on Mars.

Page 3

2 What happened just after *Pathfinder* landed on Mars?

(A) It sent images back to Earth.

(B) The lander separated from the orbiter.

(C) A parachute opened.

(D) Giant airbags opened.

3 What happened before *Spirit* and *Opportunity* got to Mars?

(A) They traveled for miles across the planet.

(B) They took pictures and collected soil.

(C) Two robots landed safely in 2004.

(D) The *Mars Polar Lander* went to Mars.

4 Which word means the same as essential in paragraph 3?

(A) There

(B) Necessary

(C) Also

(D) Helpful

5 Which word from the article means about the same as specialists in paragraph 6?

(A) *parachutes*

(B) *images*

(C) *experts*

(D) *air bags*

GO ON

© Macmillan/McGraw-Hill

6 Which word means about the same
as <u>research</u> in paragraph 7?

  A Travel

  B Study

  C Art

  D Disappearance

7 What happened when *Pathfinder* traveled to Mars? Write the events in the
order they happened. Explain your answer and support it with details from
the article.

_____

_____

_____

_____

_____

_____

_____

Page 5

GO ON ➡

Kyle wrote this report about flying. He wants you to review his report. As you read, think about the corrections and improvements that Kyle should make. Then answer the questions that follow.

Dreams of Flying

(1) I want to be a pilot someday. (2) My interest in flying comes from my family. (3) My grandfather's wish was to explore outer spase. (4) That dream never comed true.

(5) When my father growed up, he wanted to be an airplane pilot. (6) He flied for the first time when he was just sixteen years old! (7) That flight was in a small airplane named *Betty.*

(8) Now my dad works for an airline, and he travels to Japan, China, and Europe. (9) He loves to explore new places. (10) He says his favorite city of all is Tokyo, Japan.

GO ON ➡

8 What change, if any, should be made in sentence 3?

  (A) Change *grandfather's* to **Grandfather's**

  (B) Change *wish* to **wishes**

  (C) Change *spase* to **space**

  (D) Make no change

9 What change, if any, should be made in sentence 4?

  (A) Insert a comma after *dream*

  (B) Change *comed* to **came**

  (C) Change the period to a question mark

  (D) Make no change

10 What change, if any, should be made in sentence 5?

  (A) Change *father* to **Father**

  (B) Change *growed* to **grew**

  (C) Change *wanted* to **wants**

  (D) Make no change

11 What change, if any, should be made in sentence 6?

  (A) Change *flied* to **flew**

  (B) Insert a comma after *time*

  (C) Change *years* to **year**

  (D) Make no change

12 What change, if any, should be made in sentence 10?

  (A) Change *says* to **say**

  (B) Change *city* to **sity**

  (C) Take out the comma between *Tokyo* and *Japan*

  (D) Make no change

STOP

Page 7

Grade 3 • Unit 4 • Week 5
Student Evaluation Chart

Tested Skills	Number Correct	Percent Correct
Reading Comprehension: *Sequence, 1, 2, 3*	/3	%
Short Answer: *Sequence, 7*	/3	%
Vocabulary Strategies: *Thesaurus: Synonyms, 4, 5, 6*	/3	%
Grammar, Mechanics, and Usage: *Irregular Verbs, 9, 10; Correct Verb Form, 11*	/3	%
Spelling: *Words with Soft c and g, 8,12*	/2	%
Total Weekly Test Score	/14	%

Student Name _____

Date _____

Weekly Assessment

TESTED SKILLS AND STRATEGIES

- **Reading Comprehension**
- **Vocabulary Strategies**
- **Grammar, Mechanics, and Usage**
- **Spelling**

Mc Graw Hill **Macmillan/McGraw-Hill**

DIRECTIONS

Read "Life in the Cold." Then read each question. Decide which is the best answer to each question. Mark the space for the answer you have chosen. Write your answer to question 7.

Life in the Cold

1   Picture a place where nobody lives. The weather is never <u>fair</u>. This place is covered by ice. It is always below freezing. Fierce wind whips over the packed ice. This is Antarctica, the coldest place on Earth. It might not look like a desert, but it is because less than two inches of snow fall each year in Antarctica. The water is frozen into ice, so no plants can grow there.

2   The dry cold is very hard on living things. But some kinds of animals seem made for the cold. Antarctica is home to penguins, seals, and whales. Each animal has special ways to keep warm and find food.

3   Penguins have ways of staying warm. Soft feathers called *down* protect them. These feathers keep the warmer air close to their skin. A thick layer of fat helps, too. They huddle together for warmth. Hundreds of penguins stand close together on sheets of ice. These birds cannot fly. A penguin <u>shuffles</u> along over the ice but is a good swimmer. It catches fish in the icy waters. But penguins have to swim fast. Sharks live in the Antarctic waters, too, and they hunt penguins.

Page 2

GO ON ▶

Student Name _____

4　　Seals have flippers that help them swim in the freezing water. The Antarctic waters are rich in food, and seals are good hunters. Like penguins, seals have a layer of fat to keep them warm. This fat is called blubber. Seals' thick fur also keeps them warm.

5　　Some whales swim in the Antarctic waters. They feed on shrimp, crabs, and other small sea animals. Whales also have blubber to keep them warm. Whales are mammals. They must come up above the waves to breathe air. Sometimes a whale gets trapped under the ice. This is a danger because then the whale cannot reach the air.

6　　It is hard to picture a place where it is always winter. Ice stretches out for miles and miles. Most people would find it too cold to live there, but the animals who live there seem to feel right at home.

1 Read the diagram below to answer the following question.

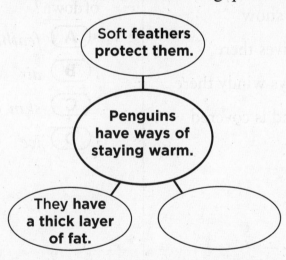

Which of these goes in the empty oval?

　(A) They cannot fly.

　(B) They shuffle over the ice.

　(C) They swim fast.

　(D) They huddle together.

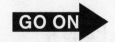

Page 3

© Macmillan/McGraw-Hill

2 Which detail best supports the idea that whales have special ways to survive in Antarctica?

(A) Whales are mammals.

(B) Whales have blubber to keep them warm.

(C) Whales must come up above the waves to breathe.

(D) Sometimes a whale gets trapped under the ice.

3 Antarctica is a desert because —

(A) it gets less than two inches of snow

(B) nobody lives there

(C) it is always windy there

(D) the ground is covered with ice

4 Which meaning of the word <u>fair</u> best fits the way it is used in paragraph 1?

(A) Pale in color, blond

(B) Clear and sunny

(C) Pretty or handsome

(D) Following the rules

5 Which word in paragraph 3 helps the reader figure out the meaning of <u>down</u>?

(A) *feathers*

(B) *air*

(C) *skin*

(D) *ice*

© Macmillan/McGraw-Hill

Page 4

GO ON →

6 In paragraph 3, the word <u>shuffles</u>
means —

    (**A**) runs quickly

    (**B**) flies gracefully

    (**C**) swims easily

    (**D**) walks slowly

7 What is the main idea of "Life in the Cold"? Explain your answer and support it with details from the article.

_____

_____

_____

_____

_____

_____

_____

Page 5

GO ON ▶

DIRECTIONS
Read the introduction and the passage that follows. Then read each question and fill in the correct answer.

Wendy wrote this letter. She wants you to review her letter. As you read, think about the corrections and improvements that Wendy should make. Then answer the questions that follow.

Dear Aunt Judith,

(1) My berthday this year was the best one I have ever had! (2) Mom, Dad, and I took a road trip. (3) We went to Old Bingham Village, a place where you can see actors dressed as people from the american revolution. (4) Each actor takes the part of a real person who lived hundreds of years ago.

(5) My favorite character was doctor Burns. (6) He told we how he had traveled over the ocean from London, England. (7) He showed us how he made medicine from plants he grew in his herb garden. (8) His hairdo was a ponytail covered with white powder!

(9) We had such a good time that we plan to return over Thanksgiving vacation.

Love,
Wendy

© Macmillan/McGraw-Hill

GO ON

8 What change, if any, should be made in sentence 1?

(A) Change *berthday* to **birthday**

(B) Change *I* to **i**

(C) Change the exclamation mark to a question mark

(D) Make no change

9 What change, if any, should be made in sentence 3?

(A) Change *Old Bingham Village* to **Old bingham village**

(B) Change *can see* to **can seeing**

(C) Change *american revolution* to **American Revolution**

(D) Make no change

10 What change, if any, should be made in sentence 5?

(A) Change *was* to **were**

(B) Insert a comma after *was*

(C) Change *doctor Burns* to **Doctor Burns**

(D) Make no change

11 What change, if any, should be made in sentence 6?

(A) Change *we* to **us**

(B) Change *ocean* to **Ocean**

(C) Change *London, England* to **London, england**

(D) Make no change

12 What change, if any, should be made in sentence 8?

(A) Change *His* to **Him**

(B) Change *hairdo* to **hairedo**

(C) Change *was* to **were**

(D) Make no change

STOP

Page 7

Grade 3 • Unit 5 • Week 1
Student Evaluation Chart

Tested Skills	Number Correct	Percent Correct
Reading Comprehension: *Main Idea and Details*, 1, 2, 3	/3	%
Short Answer: *Main Idea and Details*, 7	/3	%
Vocabulary Strategies: *Context Clues: Homographs*, 4; *Context Clues*, 5, 6	/3	%
Grammar, Mechanics, and Usage: *Capitalizing I and Proper Nouns*, 9, 10; *Pronouns*, 11	/3	%
Spelling: *Words with Closed Syllables*, 8, 12	/2	%
Total Weekly Test Score	/14	%

Student Name _____

Date _____

Weekly Assessment

TESTED SKILLS AND STRATEGIES

- **Reading Comprehension**
- **Vocabulary Strategies**
- **Grammar, Mechanics, and Usage**
- **Spelling**

DIRECTIONS

Read "The Busy Home of Honeybees." Then read each question. Decide which is the best answer to each question. Mark the space for the answer you have chosen. Write your answer to question 7.

The Busy Home of Honeybees

The queen bee is surrounded by worker bees. The queen is larger than all other bees in the nest.

1   Honeybees are interesting creatures. For example, these able architects build special nests. In the wild, a nest can contain up to 20,000 bees, but a hive built by farmers can <u>contain</u> as many as 80,000 busy insects. The honeybees live and work in these nests, which are made of waxy <u>structures</u> called honeycombs. The honey that you spread on your toast comes from these honeycombs.

2   The combs are built of flat walls made up of many shallow, six-sided <u>cells</u>. The comb has two sides, with cells on each side. All the cells are exactly the same size and are evenly spaced. The spacing between cells depends on what that side of the shelter will be used for.

3   One part of the nest, where the queen bee lays her eggs, is called the brood comb. That is where the young bees are raised. On the other side of the nest, the bees store honey and pollen.

© Macmillan/McGraw-Hill

GO ON ➡

4   There are different kinds of honeybees, but all of the bees work together to keep the nest running smoothly. To begin with, the nurse bees feed the newborn bees "royal jelly." This is a special food the worker bees make for the young bees. When the babies grow up, the male bees are called drones. They mate with the queen bee, who makes more bees. That is the queen's only job, but it is an important one.

5   Another kind of bee in the nest is the worker bee. Worker bees have important jobs, too. For example, they gather pollen and bring it back to the nest for food and to produce beeswax. They also help control the temperature of the nest. The house bees are another kind of bee. They build the comb by using their mouths to form wax into cells.

6   Many bees are needed in a nest to keep the colony alive and well. Scientists study these creatures to understand how they work so well in groups. Because the bees are so organized, they can survive in many climates. There is still much to learn about these interesting insects!

1 Look at the chart below.

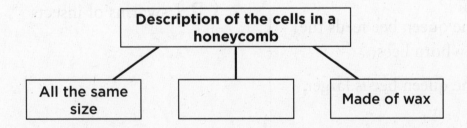

Description of the cells in a honeycomb

- All the same size
- [ ]
- Made of wax

Which of these goes in the empty box?

    A Busy insects

    B Royal jelly

    C Six-sided

    D Gather pollen

Page 3

2 In a bees' nest, the comb is made of —

- **A** wax
- **B** pollen
- **C** honey
- **D** jelly

4 Which word means the same as contain in paragraph 1?

- **A** Work
- **B** Hold
- **C** Buy
- **D** See

3 How is the queen bee different from all the other bees?

- **A** The queen bee gathers pollen.
- **B** The queen bee builds the comb.
- **C** The queen bee feeds the newborn bees.
- **D** The queen bee is larger.

5 In paragraph 1, the word structures means —

- **A** things that are built
- **B** jars of honey
- **C** types of beeswax
- **D** swarms of insects

© Macmillan/McGraw-Hill

Page 4

GO ON ➡

6 Which word is pronounced the same as <u>cells</u> in paragraph 2?

- (A) Yells
- (B) Calls
- (C) Seals
- (D) Sells

7 What are the different jobs that bees do? Explain your answer and support it with details from the article.

_____

_____

_____

_____

_____

_____

_____

Page 5

GO ON

Read the introduction and the passage that follows. Then read each question and fill in the correct answer.

Mindy wrote this story about piano lessons. She wants you to review her story. As you read, think about the corrections and improvements that Mindy should make. Then answer the questions that follow.

Piano Lessons

(1) Rebecca and I take piano lessons together every Thursday. (2) Last night she called I at 6:30 P.M. (3) Her had lost the music for today's lesson. (4) I hurryed through my practice, and then Mom took the music over to Rebecca's house.

(5) After school, I walked down the street to the Community Music Center. (6) Rebecca was waiting in the lobby with our friend Jason, and they were studying the music. (7) She handed her to me and smiled.

(8) "Thanks for sending over the music!" she exclaimed.

© Macmillan/McGraw-Hill

GO ON

8 What change, if any, should be made in sentence 2?

- **A** Change *she* to **her**
- **B** Change *called* to **calls**
- **C** Change *I* to **me**
- **D** Make no change

9 What change, if any, should be made in sentence 3?

- **A** Change *Her* to **She**
- **B** Change *today's* to **todays**
- **C** Change *lesson* to **Lesson**
- **D** Make no change

10 What change, if any, should be made in sentence 4?

- **A** Change *hurryed* to **hurried**
- **B** Take out the comma after *practice*
- **C** Change *Mom* to **mom**
- **D** Make no change

11 What change, if any, should be made in sentence 6?

- **A** Change *they* to **them**
- **B** Change *studying* to **studieing**
- **C** Change the period to a question mark
- **D** Make no change

12 What change, if any, should be made in sentence 7?

- **A** Change *her* to **it**
- **B** Change *me* to **I**
- **C** Change *smiled* to **smiling**
- **D** Make no change

Page 7

STOP

Student Name _____

Grade 3 • Unit 5 • Week 2
Student Evaluation Chart

Tested Skills	Number Correct	Percent Correct
Reading Comprehension: *Description, 1, 2; Compare and Contrast, 3*	/3	%
Short Answer: *Description, 7*	/3	%
Vocabulary Strategies: *Context Clues, 4, 5; Context Clues: Homophones, 6*	/3	%
Grammar, Mechanics, and Usage: *Subject and Object Pronouns, 8, 9; Pronoun Usage, 12*	/3	%
Spelling: *Words with inflectional Endings, Changing y to i, 10, 11*	/2	%
Total Weekly Test Score	/14	%

Student Name _____

Date _____

Weekly Assessment

TESTED SKILLS AND STRATEGIES

- **Reading Comprehension**
- **Vocabulary Strategies**
- **Grammar, Mechanics, and Usage**
- **Spelling**

Mc Graw Hill **Macmillan/McGraw-Hill**

DIRECTIONS

Read "African Elephants." Then read each question. Decide which is the best answer to each question. Mark the space for the answer you have chosen. Write your answer to question 7.

African Elephants

1   Africa is almost twice the size of the United States. It has deserts, grasslands, and rainforests. Africa has cities and towns much like those here. The continent of Africa is also home to the largest land mammal in the world—the elephant.

2   Most African elephants live in the grasslands where there is enough rain and plenty of space for these enormous creatures to move around. Elephants are huge! An adult male elephant can grow to be more than 10 feet tall and weigh almost 12,000 pounds. What's more, these creatures never stop growing! You can always spot the oldest elephant in a herd because it will be the biggest one. An elephant can <u>survive</u> for up to 60 years.

3   Another way to determine an elephant's age is by its tusks. Male and female African elephants have long, curved tusks growing on either side of their faces. Elephants use their tusks to knock down trees. Sometimes you will see an elephant with one very long tusk and one very short tusk. The short one has been worn down or broken during the elephant's many years of tree

Page 2

GO ON

toppling. And why do they tear down trees? To eat them! Elephants eat the trunks of trees as well as the leaves, branches, and bark.

4   Elephants have another tool to topple trees, too. Their trunks! Elephants are known for their very long noses. An adult elephant can use its trunk to snap a foot-thick tree or to pick up something as small as a peanut. When it has not rained in a long time, elephants can use their trunks to dig deep holes in the ground in search of water.

5   How else do elephants find water when it has not rained? They live in family groups called herds. The oldest female elephant in the group leads the herd. She is called the matriarch. She can remember where every source of water is for miles around! Some elephants have found watering holes they have not visited in 20 years.

6   The matriarch has another crucial job. She helps raise all of the baby elephants in the herd. Baby elephants are called calves. A newborn calf weighs almost 250 pounds! Although the matriarch is not the mother to each calf, it is her job to keep each one safe. She also teaches the younger female elephants how to care for the calves.

7   Elephants are truly amazing animals.

GO ON

1 What is the most likely reason an elephant would have two different-sized tusks?

(A) One tusk broke when knocking down trees.

(B) One tusk got worn down from digging holes.

(C) One tusk fell out when the elephant got old.

(D) One tusk did not grow as quickly as the other.

2 Elephants tear down trees to —

(A) fight other elephants

(B) eat the bark and leaves

(C) dig for water

(D) make pens for baby elephants

3 Which word best describes African elephants?

(A) Angry

(B) Careful

(C) Lazy

(D) Powerful

4 What does the word <u>survive</u> mean in paragraph 2?

(A) Hunt

(B) Remember

(C) Live

(D) Search

GO ON

Page 4

5 In paragraph 5, the word source means —

(A) a way to use

(B) a place to find

(C) a map that shows

(D) an animal that shares

6 Which word means the same as crucial in paragraph 6?

(A) Easy

(B) New

(C) Important

(D) Famous

7 Why do African elephants live in the grasslands? Explain your answer and support it with details from the article.

_____

_____

_____

_____

_____

_____

_____

Page 5

GO ON ▶

Read the introduction and the passage that follows. Then read each question and fill in the correct answer.

Jill wrote this story about a birthday card. She wants you to review her story. As you read, think about corrections and improvements that Jill should make. Then answer the questions that follow.

A Card for Ketia

(1) Today I will write a leter and make a card for my friend Ketia, who lives in Nebraska. (2) It is her birthday next Wednesday. (3) I is going to decorate the card with stickers. (4) The stickers are really cute. (5) They is in the shape of balloons and animals. (6) My favorite animal stickers are a bird, a pig, and a rabbit.

(7) I think Ketia will be happy to get my birthday card. (8) She moved away last fall, and she feel a little lonely. (9) I hope she can come back for a visit next summer.

© Macmillan/McGraw-Hill

Page 6

GO ON ➡️

8 What change, if any, should be made in sentence 1?

- **A** Change *I* to *i*
- **B** Change *leter* to **letter**
- **C** Change *Nebraska* to **nebraska**
- **D** Make no change

9 What change, if any, should be made in sentence 3?

- **A** Change *is* to **am**
- **B** Change *going* to **gone**
- **C** Change the period to a question mark
- **D** Make no change

10 What change, if any, should be made in sentence 5?

- **A** Change *is* to **are**
- **B** Insert a comma after *balloons*
- **C** Change *animals* to **animales**
- **D** Make no change

11 What change, if any, should be made in sentence 6?

- **A** Change *are* to **is**
- **B** Take out the comma after *bird*
- **C** Change *rabbit* to **rabit**
- **D** Make no change

12 What change, if any, should be made in sentence 8?

- **A** Change *moved* to **moves**
- **B** Take out the comma after *fall*
- **C** Change *feel* to **feels**
- **D** Make no change

STOP

Page 7

Grade 3 • Unit 5 • Week 3
Student Evaluation Chart

Tested Skills	Number Correct	Percent Correct
Reading Comprehension: *Cause and Effect*, 1, 2; *Draw Conclusions*, 3	/3	%
Short Answer: *Cause and Effect*, 7	/3	%
Vocabulary Strategies: *Context Clues*, 4, 5; *Context Clues: Synonyms*, 6	/3	%
Grammar, Mechanics, and Usage: *Pronoun-Verb Agreement*, 9, 10, 12	/3	%
Spelling: *Words with Closed Syllables*, 8, 11	/2	%
Total Weekly Test Score	/14	%

Student Name _____

Date _____

Weekly Assessment

TESTED SKILLS AND STRATEGIES

- **Reading Comprehension**
- **Vocabulary Strategies**
- **Grammar, Mechanics, and Usage**
- **Spelling**

Macmillan/McGraw-Hill

DIRECTIONS

Read "A Lesson Learned." Then read each question. Decide which is the best answer to each question. Mark the space for the answer you have chosen. Write your answer to question 7.

A Lesson Learned

1   There once lived a wealthy man named Katu, who thought that everything he owned was better than everything that anyone else owned. He wanted only the finest of everything, and he made sure his neighbors knew that he had it.

2   Katu had an elegant home, but he did not think it was good enough. So, one day he decided to build a new house. It would be made of tall logs, and of course Katu was soon boasting that his logs were the best money could buy.

3   To move the logs, Katu hired a man who owned an elephant named Lago, the strongest elephant anyone had ever seen. All the people in the village were amazed when they saw how easily Lago handled the weighty logs. While Lago piled the logs higher and higher to make the house, Katu stood nearby, having a conversation with two other men. Soon, of course, he was boasting that his house was going to be the best house in the village.

© Macmillan/McGraw-Hill

GO ON

4   "You see, my friends," said Katu, "how wonderful my house will be. There will be none other like it in the whole village."

5   What Katu did not know was that there was something extraordinary about Lago aside from his amazing strength. Lago understood every word that Katu was saying, and the elephant did not like what he was hearing. Katu continued to brag, and Lago soon decided that he had heard enough.

6   Katu was still boasting when one of the men interrupted him by pointing wildly over his shoulder.

7   "What is it?" Katu asked, very annoyed at the interruption. When the man kept pointing, Katu finally turned around. In the next moment, he forgot all about what he was saying.

8   Lago was coming straight at him! The others quickly scrambled out of the way, but Katu was too amazed to move. In an instant, Lago seized Katu in his trunk and lifted him high in the air. Soon Lago was standing right next to the unlucky man's house, which was almost completed.

9   Holding Katu so that he looked down at his new house, Lago bumped into it hard. The house began to sway and then collapsed in a heap of logs. Then Lago set Katu gently on the ground.

10   It took Katu weeks to rebuild his house, but he learned his lesson. From that day on, he never uttered another boast.

Page 3

1 Why does Katu say that his things are better than everyone else's?

    A He wants to sell his things.

    B He wants people to think he's important.

    C He wants to give his things away.

    D He wants to make other people feel better.

2 Why does one of the men point wildly at Katu?

    A He sees that Katu's house is falling.

    B He is angry at Katu for bragging.

    C He sees Lago coming straight at Katu.

    D He knows the elephant cannot lift the logs.

3 Why does Lago do what he does to Katu?

    A Katu once treated him badly.

    B He wants to teach Katu a lesson.

    C He is tired of building Katu's house.

    D Katu is not going to pay Lago's owner.

4 Which word means the same as seized in paragraph 8?

    A Helped

    B Checked

    C Pushed

    D Grabbed

GO ON

5 In paragraph 8, the word unlucky means —

(A) not lucky

(B) with luck

(C) lucky again

(D) already lucky

6 In paragraph 10, the word rebuild means —

(A) build again

(B) build well

(C) not build

(D) one who builds

7 What were the other men probably thinking and feeling when they saw Lago knock down Katu's house? Explain your answer and support it with details from the story.

_____

_____

_____

_____

_____

_____

Page 5

GO ON ➡

DIRECTIONS

Read the introduction and the passage that follows. Then read each question
and fill in the correct answer.

*Bruce wrote this story about a dog. He wants you to review his
story. As you read, think about the corrections and improvements
that Bruce should make. Then answer the questions that follow.*

Butch

(1) Mr. and Mrs. Bellamy asked David to take they new dog for
a walk. (2) The dog is namd Butch, and he is a breed called a Great
Dane. (3) Butch is a big dog, and he coat is black and white. (4) There
is only one problem with Butch. (5) Sometimes he is too friendly!

(6) Yesterday David was walking Butch down Main Street when
a woman passed them on the sidewalk. (7) Butch acted so friendly
that he got his leash wraped around the woman's legs. (8) David
said he was sorry. (9) The woman said, "That's okay, your dog is
just friendly."

Page 6

GO ON

8 What change, if any, should be made in sentence 1?

(A) Change *Mr. and Mrs.* to **mr. and mrs.**

(B) Change *asked* to **asking**

(C) Change *they* to **their**

(D) Make no change

9 What change, if any, should be made in sentence 2?

(A) Change *namd* to **named**

(B) Take out the comma after *Butch*

(C) Change *called* to **calling**

(D) Make no change

10 What change, if any, should be made in sentence 3?

(A) Take out the comma after *dog*

(B) Change *he* to **his**

(C) Change *coat* to **coats**

(D) Make no change

11 What change, if any, should be made in sentence 7?

(A) Change *got* to **getted**

(B) Change *wraped* to **wrapped**

(C) Change *woman's* to **womans**

(D) Make no change

12 What change, if any, should be made in sentence 9?

(A) Change *That's* to **Thats**

(B) Take out the quotation marks

(C) Change *your* to **you**

(D) Make no change

Page 7

STOP

Grade 3 • Unit 5 • Week 4
Student Evaluation Chart

Tested Skills	Number Correct	Percent Correct
Reading Comprehension: *Draw Conclusions*, 1, 2, 3	/3	%
Short Answer: *Draw Conclusions*, 7	/3	%
Vocabulary Strategies: *Context Clues, 4; Prefixes re-, un-, dis-, pre-, 5, 6*	/3	%
Grammar, Mechanics, and Usage: *Possessive Pronouns, 8, 10, 12;*	/3	%
Spelling: *Words with Inflectional Endings, 9, 11*	/2	%
Total Weekly Test Score	/14	%

Student Name _____

Date _____

Weekly Assessment

TESTED SKILLS AND STRATEGIES

- • Reading Comprehension
- • Vocabulary Strategies
- • Grammar, Mechanics, and Usage
- • Spelling

Macmillan/McGraw-Hill

DIRECTIONS

Read "Mammoth Cave." Then read each question. Decide which is the best answer to each question. Mark the space for the answer you have chosen. Write your answer to question 7.

Mammoth Cave

1   Did you know that the longest cave in the world is in Kentucky? Mammoth Cave is over 365 miles long. The cave has many levels, one on top of the other. These layers have been forming very slowly over the past 350 million years.

2   Some parts of Mammoth Cave have tight passages and tiny spaces. Other parts of the cave are huge, empty rooms. People can visit Mammoth Cave and take a tour of these vast underground spaces. Visitors can sit in a room and listen as their guide tells about how the caves were formed.

3   It is an interesting story. The caves were formed by underground water. Over time, the water drained deeper and deeper into the earth. It slowly dripped down through holes and cracks in the ground. Bit by bit, the dripping water carved out caves and passages. The upper levels of the cave are mostly dry because the water drained out of those areas many years ago. The lower levels are still wet.

Page 2

GO ON

4   As the water flowed, it carried tiny pieces of rocks. Over millions of years, the tiny pieces formed many shapes. If you visit the caves today, you will see many interesting formations. Two related types are stalactites and stalagmites. Both are types of spikes, but they are not identical. Stalactites are spikes that grow downward. Stalagmites are spikes that grow upward. There are also many "drip curtains" and small, sharp needles that have formed within the cave. One drip curtain looks a lot like a waterfall. It is about 75 feet high and 50 feet wide. It is called Frozen Niagara because people thought it looked like Niagara Falls. It is an amazing sight.

5   These stone shapes aren't the only things in Mammoth Cave. About 200 different kinds of animals have been discovered there. Some animals, such as raccoons, bats, and cave crickets, use the cave just for shelter. They get their food outside and then return to the cave to sleep or rest.

6   Some animals can live only in the cave. They have become so good at cave life that they could not live anywhere else. Because the cave is always dark, they do not need to blend in with their surroundings. For this reason, many of them are very pale. Some of them do not even have eyes! There are eyeless fish and eyeless shrimp that live in the underground rivers.

7   The water in Mammoth Cave is still flowing, so the caves are still forming. Scientists also believe there could be hundreds of miles of cave that have not been discovered yet. So the next time you are in Kentucky, visit Mammoth Cave and discover something new!

GO ON

Page 3

1 The upper levels of Mammoth Cave are different from the lower levels because they are —

(**A**) only a few years old

(**B**) still wet

(**C**) not underground

(**D**) mostly dry

2 How are stalactites and stalagmites alike?

(**A**) Both grow upward.

(**B**) Both grow downward.

(**C**) Both are spikes.

(**D**) Both are curtains.

3 The interesting shapes in the cave were formed by tiny pieces of rock carried by —

(**A**) water

(**B**) wind

(**C**) animals

(**D**) people

4 What definition from the dictionary fits the word <u>related</u> in paragraph 4?

(**A**) Beautiful or pretty

(**B**) Soft to the touch

(**C**) Made a long time ago

(**D**) Connected in some way

GO ON →

5 What definition fits the word
identical in paragraph 4?

- **A** Made of rock
- **B** Easy to see
- **C** Exactly the same
- **D** Under the ground

6 Which definition of the word
sight fits the way it is used in
paragraph 4?

- **A** The power of seeing
- **B** Something seen
- **C** A personal view
- **D** A kind of tool

7 How are the animals that live only in the cave different from animals that
live outside the cave? Explain your answer and support it with details from
the article.

_____

_____

_____

_____

_____

_____

_____

Page 5

GO ON ➡

DIRECTIONS
Read the introduction and the passage that follows. Then read each question and fill in the correct answer.

Harry wrote this story about some lost keys. He wants you to review his story. As you read, think about the corrections and improvements that Harry should make. Then answer the questions that follow.

The Lost Keys

(1) Mom and Dad are late wherever they go. (2) I bet you wonder what they're problem is. (3) Its that they are always losing the keys to the car! (4) Sometimes I think they are the most forgetful people on the plannet!

(5) Yesterday, the three of us went out to have lunch at our favorite restaurant. (6) It is the Greek dinner on Center Avenue. (7) We had a great time until the meal was over. (8) Mom said, "Oh, no, I can't find the keys to the car!"

(9) Luckily, I was there. (10) I said, "The keys are in you're handbag."

Page 6

GO ON

8 What change, if any, should be made in sentence 2?

  (A) Insert a comma after *wonder*

  (B) Change *they're* to **their**

  (C) Change *is* to **are**

  (D) Make no change

9 What change, if any, should be made in sentence 3?

  (A) Change *Its* to **It's**

  (B) Change *they are* to **their**

  (C) Change the exclamation mark to a question mark

  (D) Make no change

10 What change, if any, should be made in sentence 4?

  (A) Insert a comma after *think*

  (B) Change *they* to **them**

  (C) Change *plannet* to **planet**

  (D) Make no change

11 What change, if any, should be made in sentence 6?

  (A) Change *dinner* to **diner**

  (B) Change *Avenue* to **avenue**

  (C) Change the period to a question mark

  (D) Make no change

12 What change, if any, should be made in sentence 10?

  (A) Change *said* to **sayed**

  (B) Change *in* to **inn**

  (C) Change *you're* to **your**

  (D) Make no change

STOP

Student Name _____

Grade 3 • Unit 5 • Week 5
Student Evaluation Chart

Tested Skills	Number Correct	Percent Correct
Reading Comprehension: *Compare and Contrast, 1, 2; Cause and Effect, 3*	/3	%
Short Answer: *Compare and Contrast, 7*	/3	%
Vocabulary Strategies: *Dictionary: Unknown Words, 4, 5; Context Clues: Multiple-Meaning Words, 6*	/3	%
Grammar, Mechanics, and Usage: *Contractions and Possessive Pronouns, 8, 12; Spelling Contractions and Possessive Pronouns, 9*	/3	%
Spelling: *Words With Open Syllables, 10, 11*	/2	%
Total Weekly Test Score	/14	%

Student Name _____

Date _____

Weekly Assessment
TESTED SKILLS AND STRATEGIES

- **Reading Comprehension**
- **Vocabulary Strategies**
- **Grammar, Mechanics, and Usage**
- **Spelling**

DIRECTIONS

Read "The Banquet." Then read each question. Decide which is the best answer to each question. Mark the space for the answer you have chosen. Write your answer to question 7.

The Banquet

1   In September, Mitsuko Kojima moved to the United States. What a change! Japan was so far away. Mitsuko wrote letters to her friends and looked at pictures of her old house. She looked out the window at the strange street below and felt sad.

2   She missed her old schoolmates, but her new school was okay. The new children were friendly, and the teacher was also <u>agreeable</u>. Mitsuko spoke some English, and her parents spoke a little, too. "You will learn quickly," they said. "Children learn more quickly than grownups." Her English got better little by little.

3   Mitsuko walked home after school one day and sat down next to her mother.

4   "What did you have for lunch today?" said her mother.

5   "A sandwich," answered Mitsuko.

6   "Was it good?"

GO ON

7   "It was okay." Mitsuko thought of spicy crab rolls and hot fish soup and delicious tuna with special sauce. Her loneliness got mixed up with the dream of a good meal.

8   One day her mother said, "I am giving a special <u>banquet</u>. Our neighbors will come, and I'll ask everyone to bring some food."

9   Mrs. Kojima cooked for two days to make all of Mitsuko's favorite dishes. The house smelled delicious. It smelled like Japan.

10   The guests brought their favorite dishes. Some brought soups, while others came with roasted chicken. One person brought pizza, and there were sweet potatoes, salads, and pies. All this and more was on the Kojimas' table. All the guests were talking and laughing. "Trying so many different dishes makes this a wonderful feast!" they said. "What a good idea Mrs. Kojima had!"

11   At first Mitsuko could only <u>gaze</u> with curiosity at the table. She was not untrusting, but the food looked odd. She stared at the food as she remembered her meals back in Japan.

12   Finally, she put a little food on a plate. She decided to try a bit of everything. A crab roll sat next to a French fry, while a sweet potato snuggled up to pizza. This was a mixed-up meal! They had not eaten like this in Japan. Mitsuko giggled and showed her mother the plate.

13   "Is it good?" Mrs. Kojima asked.

14   "Yes, it is good," Mitsuko said with a smile.

Page 3

GO ON

1 At the beginning of the story, the reader can tell that —

- **A** Mitsuko feels homesick for Japan
- **B** Mitsuko's mother is making her angry
- **C** Mitsuko's new school is too difficult for her
- **D** Mitsuko will not try food from the United States

2 Why does Mrs. Kojima ask the neighbors to bring food to the banquet?

- **A** She wants Mitsuko to eat more so she will be healthy.
- **B** She wants to help Mitsuko get used to the food in her new country.
- **C** She does not think the neighbors will like the food she has cooked.
- **D** She does not want the neighbors to eat all the food she made for Mitsuko.

3 How do the guests feel about Mrs. Kojima's party?

- **A** They do not like such a mixed-up meal.
- **B** They wish that all of the food could be Japanese.
- **C** They only want to eat the food that they brought.
- **D** They enjoyed having many kinds of food to choose from.

4 Which word from the story means about the same as agreeable in paragraph 2?

- **A** strange
- **B** favorite
- **C** friendly
- **D** special

GO ON

Page 4

5 Which word from the story means the same as the word banquet in paragraph 8?

(A) house

(B) picture

(C) dream

(D) feast

6 Which word means the same as gaze in paragraph 11?

(A) Stare

(B) Blink

(C) Frown

(D) Nod

7 By the end of the story, how have Mitsuko's feelings changed? Explain your answer and support it with details from the story.

_____

_____

_____

_____

_____

_____

_____

GO ON

Read the introduction and the passage that follows. Then read each question and fill in the correct answer.

Clay wrote this story about going to the library. He wants you to review his story. As you read, think about the corrections and improvements that Clay should make. Then answer the questions that follow.

The Library

(1) Every Thursday, our teacher, Mrs. Martinez, takes us to the school library. (2) The librarian's name is Mr Tran. (3) At the library, we retern the books that we borrowed last week. (4) Then we go to the shelves and look for an new book to take out. (5) This week I chose an exciting book called <u>voyage to the chocolate planet</u>.

(6) When everyone has a book, we sit on the beanbag chairs in the reading area. (7) Then the librarian reads aloud to us for fifteen minutes. (8) He used to let kids vote on the book, but everyone would dissagree. (9) Now he picks the book, and we usually like his choice.

GO ON

© Macmillan/McGraw-Hill

8 What change, if any, should be made in sentence 2?

   (**A**) Change *librarian's* to **librarians**

   (**B**) Change *is* to **are**

   (**C**) Change *Mr* to **Mr.**

   (**D**) Make no change

9 What change, if any, should be made in sentence 3?

   (**A**) Change *retern* to **return**

   (**B**) Change *books* to **book's**

   (**C**) Change *we* to **us**

   (**D**) Make no change

10 What change, if any, should be made in sentence 4?

   (**A**) Change *go* to **going**

   (**B**) Change *shelves* to **shelfs**

   (**C**) Change *an* to **a**

   (**D**) Make no change

11 What change, if any, should be made in sentence 5?

   (**A**) Change *an* to **a**

   (**B**) Change *voyage to the chocolate planet* to Voyage to the Chocolate Planet

   (**C**) Change the period to an exclamation mark

   (**D**) Make no change

12 What change, if any, should be made in sentence 8?

   (**A**) Change *kids* to **kid's**

   (**B**) Take out the comma after *book*

   (**C**) Change *dissagree* to **disagree**

   (**D**) Make no change

STOP

© Macmillan/McGraw-Hill

Page 7

Grade 3 • Unit 6 • Week 1
Student Evaluation Chart

Tested Skills	Number Correct	Percent Correct
Reading Comprehension: *Make Inferences, 1, 2, 3*	/3	%
Short Answer: *Make Inferences, 7*	/3	%
Vocabulary Strategies: *Context Clues: Synonyms, 4, 5, 6*	/3	%
Grammar, Mechanics, and Usage: *Titles and Abbreviations, 8, 11; Adjectives and Articles, 10*	/3	%
Spelling: *Words with Prefixes (re-, un-, pre-, dis-, de-), 9, 12*	/2	%
Total Weekly Test Score	/14	%

Student Name _____

Date _____

Weekly Assessment

TESTED SKILLS AND STRATEGIES

- **Reading Comprehension**
- **Vocabulary Strategies**
- **Grammar, Mechanics, and Usage**
- **Spelling**

Macmillan/McGraw-Hill

DIRECTIONS

Read "The Thanksgiving Play." Then read each question. Decide which is the best answer to each question. Mark the space for the answer you have chosen. Write your answer to question 7.

The Thanksgiving Play

1   Mrs. Cook was worried about the Thanksgiving play. The third graders were having trouble. On Monday, Julie said that she did not want to play the part of the mother. "All I get to do is stir the soup pot," she said crossly. "And then I just tell everyone to enjoy the meal."

2   "But you are doing an important job," Mrs. Cook said. She had just been securing a paper pumpkin to the window. "You're in charge of making the feast."

3   "And I don't want to be a Pilgrim!" shouted Mark. He placed his hands on his hips and shook his head. He was the angriest of them all.

4   Everyone else started to argue. Some students tried to make their arguments the strongest , but even the weakest voice spoke up. Mrs. Cook put her hands to her ears. "Children!" she said loudly. "We have a play to put on. We have to work together now."

5   "Do we have to do this play?" Kea asked. "Everybody knows the Thanksgiving story, anyway."

GO ON

© Macmillan/McGraw-Hill

6   Mrs. Cook sighed. In her kindest voice, she pointed out, "Thanksgiving is the time we give thanks for all we have."

7   Tariq said, "Let's write a new play! It can be set in today's times. We can each write our own lines."

8   "We can still have a feast, though. While we eat we can talk about what is important to us," added Karen. "We can say what we give thanks for."

9   The class was getting excited now. Everyone liked the new idea.

10   "I give thanks for snowy days," said one student.

11   "I give thanks for my little brother," said another.

12   "Write it all down," Mrs. Cook said.

13   So the third-graders got busy writing. Then they practiced their lines happily. Everyone worked on writing the new play.

14   Wednesday was the day of the play. After they had <u>decorated</u> the stage with symbols of the holiday, the children stood behind the curtain and admired how lovely the stage looked. It was the prettiest they had ever seen it.

15   "Places, everyone," Mrs. Cook whispered as she flipped the light switch.

16   The room <u>darkened</u>, and the curtain rose. The audience saw a row of smiling faces. The Thanksgiving play was about to begin.

GO ON

Page 3

1 Read the first sentence of the summary below.

Summary

Summary of "The Thanksgiving Play"

Mrs. Cook wants her third graders to work
on the Thanksgiving play.

Which of the following completes the summary above?

A Julie does not like the part she has to play. Mrs. Cook puts a pumpkin on the window.

B Kea says that everyone knows the Thanksgiving story. One student gives thanks for snowy days.

C The children don't want to do this play. They decide to write a new play that is different.

D Wednesday is the day of the play. The children go on stage and stand behind the curtain.

---

2 At the beginning of the story, Mrs. Cook is —

A excited about the play

B amused by the children

C proud of the children

D worried about the play

3 Which word from the story means the opposite of weakest in paragraph 4?

A angriest

B kindest

C prettiest

D strongest

Page 4

GO ON ➤

4 Which sentence best tells about the new play the students write?

(A) It is set in today's times, and the children tell why they are thankful.

(B) The students give thanks for snowy days and little brothers.

(C) It takes place in the time of the Pilgrims and includes a big feast.

(D) The students tell why November is their favorite month.

5 In paragraph 14, the word <u>decorated</u> means —

(A) filled up

(B) made beautiful

(C) cleaned off

(D) made larger

6 Which word means the opposite of <u>darkened</u> in paragraph 16?

(A) Quieted

(B) Brightened

(C) Filled

(D) Disappeared

7 What happens in Mrs. Cook's classroom after the children decide to write a new play? Write a summary telling what happens.

_____

_____

_____

_____

_____

Page 5

GO ON ▶

DIRECTIONS
Read the introduction and the passage that follows. Then read each question and fill in the correct answer.

Shay wrote this essay about holidays. She wants you to review her essay. As you read, think about the corrections and improvements that Shay should make. Then answer the questions that follow.

Holidays

(1) Most people like the big, important holidays, like Fourth of July and Thanksgiving. (2) My favorite holidays are the little ones! (3) Of all the days in the year, I think May Day is the goodest. (4) On the first of May, I gather purpel flowers, put them into baskets, and deliver them to my neighbors. (5) I think this is funner than eating turkey!

(6) Another holiday I enjoy is April Fool's Day. (7) Last year I thought of a trick to play on my father. (8) I put itching powder on his towell, and that morning he had to take a second shower! (9) He laughed and said it was the baddest trick anyone had ever played on him. (10) He says he's going to get me next April!

Page 6

GO ON

© Macmillan/McGraw-Hill

8 What change, if any, should be made in sentence 3?

   A Change *May Day* to **may day**

   B Change *think* to **thinks**

   C Change *goodest* to **best**

   D Make no change

9 What change, if any, should be made in sentence 4?

   A Change *purpel* to **purple**

   B Take out the comma after *flowers*

   C Change *put* to **puts**

   D Make no change

10 What is the **BEST** way to rewrite sentence 5?

   A I thinks this is funner than eating turkey.

   B I think this is more funner than eating turkey.

   C I think this is funnest than eating turkey.

   D I think this is more fun than eating turkey.

11 What change, if any, should be made in sentence 8?

   A Change *towell* to **towel**

   B Change *he* to **they**

   C Change *had* to **has**

   D Make no change

12 What change, if any, should be made in sentence 9?

   A Change *said* to **sayed**

   B Change *baddest* to **worst**

   C Change *him* to **he**

   D Make no change

STOP

Grade 3 • Unit 6 • Week 2
Student Evaluation Chart

Tested Skills	Number Correct	Percent Correct
Reading Comprehension: *Summarize, 1, 4; Character, Setting, and Plot, 2*	/3	%
Short Answer: *Summarize, 7*	/3	%
Vocabulary Strategies: *Context Clues: Antonyms, 3, 6; Context Clues, 5*	/3	%
Grammar, Mechanics, and Usage: *Adjectives That Compare, 8, 12; Correct Comparative and Superlative Adjectives, 10*	/3	%
Spelling: *Words with Consonants + -le (al, el) Syllables, 9, 11*	/2	%
Total Weekly Test Score	/14	%

Student Name _____

Date _____

Weekly Assessment

TESTED SKILLS AND STRATEGIES

- **Reading Comprehension**
- **Vocabulary Strategies**
- **Grammar, Mechanics, and Usage**
- **Spelling**

Macmillan/McGraw-Hill

DIRECTIONS

Read "Two Writers." Then read each question. Decide which is the best answer to each question. Mark the space for the answer you have chosen. Write your answer to question 7.

Two Writers

1   Some of the most popular books children read today came from two writers: Charles Dickens and Alan Alexander Milne. You probably know some of their books. Both writers lived in England, but their stories were very different.

2   Charles Dickens was born in England in 1812. His family moved to London when he was two years old. His family was poor, so Dickens had to get a job when he was only 12 years old. He worked in a factory. Then, as a young man, Dickens worked as a newspaper reporter. He became famous as a writer when he was only 24 years old.

3   Dickens wrote 20 novels as well as many other books. His childhood helped him become an <u>insightful</u> writer whose stories told of poor families, orphans, and living in the city. For example, his second novel was *Oliver Twist*. Published in 1838, this novel tells the story of an orphan boy. Young Oliver lives in an awful workhouse, and an <u>unkind</u> man treats him terribly. It is not until the end of the novel that he finds happiness with a loving family.

GO ON

Page 2

4 In another story, *A Christmas Carol,* Dickens writes about an uncaring rich man named Scrooge who is mean to the poor and needy. Scrooge learns some hard lessons in the book and becomes a better person.

5 In the <u>majority</u> of his novels, Dickens showed how badly poor people, children, and workers were treated in England. By writing most of his books this way, Dickens helped people realize that others were being treated unfairly. Some of his books made people want to investigate living conditions in the city and try to make the world a better place.

6 Unlike Dickens, Milne wrote mostly children's stories about talking animals. His most popular stories tell about the adventures of Christopher Robin and a bear named Winnie-the-Pooh. In the stories, the boy and the bear play with their friends in the pretty woods. Some of their friends include a donkey, an owl, and a pig.

7 Alan Alexander Milne was born in 1882 in London. His father was the schoolmaster of a private school, and his family was fairly well off. After going to school in London and Cambridge, Milne got a job working for a magazine. Then he started writing plays. He soon became known as A.A. Milne.

8 Later, Milne married a woman named Daphne, and they had a son named Christopher. Christopher got a teddy bear from his father for his first birthday. It was named Winnie-the-Pooh, and it was Christopher's favorite toy. Christopher got a toy donkey named Eeyore and a toy pig named Piglet. These toys all became characters in Milne's stories. He made them into characters that could walk and talk. Christopher was in the stories, too.

9 Christopher loved the stories about Winnie-the-Pooh. Other children loved them, too. Even grownups loved them. They still bring happiness to people today.

GO ON

Page 3

1 How were Charles Dickens and A.A. Milne alike?

A Both worked in factories.

B Both got teddy bears as gifts.

C Both grew up as orphans.

D Both were writers from England.

2 How was Charles Dickens's childhood different from A.A. Milne's?

A He went to a private school.

B His family was poor.

C He lived in the country.

D His father was a schoolmaster.

3 Unlike Dickens, Milne wrote stories about —

A talking animals

B poor families

C mean rich men

D city life

4 In paragraph 3, the word <u>insightful</u> means —

A very exciting

B showing understanding

C rich or wealthy

D caring about others

GO ON ➡

Page 4

5 In paragraph 3, the word <u>unkind</u>
means —

(**A**) very kind

(**B**) one who is kind

(**C**) not kind

(**D**) in a kind way

6 What does the word <u>majority</u> mean
in paragraph 5?

(**A**) The longest

(**B**) The best selling

(**C**) The last

(**D**) The greater number

7 How were the stories of Charles Dickens and A.A. Milne alike, and how were
they different? Explain your answer and support it with details from the article.

_____

_____

_____

_____

_____

_____

_____

GO ON ▶

Page 5

DIRECTIONS

Read the introduction and the passage that follows. Then read each question and fill in the correct answer.

Chad wrote this story about the Inuit. He wants you to review his paper. As you read, think about the corrections and improvements that Chad should make. Then answer the questions that follow.

The Inuit People

(1) For hundreds of years, the Inuit people have lived in one of the coldest places on Earth. (2) They have found ways to live on frozen land far to the north, and they will remaine there. (3) The Inuit houses are made of snow or earth and are strong built. (4) The people live mainly by hunting and fishing. (5) They hunt whales, seals, and the herds of caribou that appeer every spring.

(6) The Inuit make useful tools from stone, bone, and iron. (7) They use these tools to make things and to carve beautifuly objects. (8) Groups of Inuit people who live along the coast sometimes trade with one another.

© Macmillan/McGraw-Hill

Page 6

GO ON ➡

8 What change, if any, should be made in sentence 2?

    A Change *have* to **has**

    B Change *live* to **living**

    C Change *remaine* to **remain**

    D Make no change

9 What change, if any, should be made in sentence 3?

    A Change *made* to **maked**

    B Change *strong* to **strongly**

    C Change the period to a question mark

    D Make no change

10 What change, if any, should be made in sentence 5?

    A Change *They* to **them**

    B Take out the comma after *whales*

    C Change *appeer* to **appear**

    D Make no change

11 What change, if any, should be made in sentence 6?

    A Change *make* to **makes**

    B Change *useful* to **usefully**

    C Take out the comma after *stone*

    D Make no change

12 What change, if any, should be made in sentence 7?

    A Change *use* to **uses**

    B Change *carve* to **carved**

    C Change *beautifully* to **beautiful**

    D Make no change

STOP

Page 7

Grade 3 • Unit 6 • Week 3
Student Evaluation Chart

Tested Skills	Number Correct	Percent Correct
Reading Comprehension: *Compare and Contrast (non-fiction), 1, 2, 3*	/3	%
Short Answer: *Compare and Contrast (non-fiction), 7*	/3	%
Vocabulary Strategies: *Context Clues, 4, 6; Word Parts: Prefixes and Suffixes, 5*	/3	%
Grammar, Mechanics, and Usage: *Adverbs, 9; Adjectives and Adverbs, 11, 12*	/3	%
Spelling: *Words with Vowel Team Syllables, 8, 10*	/2	%
Total Weekly Test Score	**/14**	**%**

Student Name _____

Date _____

Weekly Assessment

TESTED SKILLS AND STRATEGIES

- **Reading Comprehension**
- **Vocabulary Strategies**
- **Grammar, Mechanics, and Usage**
- **Spelling**

Macmillan/McGraw-Hill

DIRECTIONS

Read "Green Juice?" Then read each question. Decide which is the best answer to each question. Mark the space for the answer you have chosen. Write your answer to question 7.

Green Juice?

1   Every night, someone in the family made the juice the Willets had with dinner. Tonight was Eddie's turn, and he decided to surprise everyone by making something they had never seen—green juice.

2   His sister Marcy could not believe he was going to do this. Eddie did a lot of strange things, but this time, he had gone too far. "Have you lost your marbles?" she asked, staring at him with her mouth open.

3   "No," he told her. "I have all the ingredients ready. All I have to do is follow one of these recipes that I found in a magazine." He showed her a page ripped from a recent issue.

4   "I don't want to drink green juice," Marcy said with a frown. Her stomach turned at the thought of it.

5   "How do you know it won't be very tasty?" Eddie asked.

6   "Juice is supposed to be orange, or purple, or red," Marcy replied. "It's not supposed to be green!"

Page 2

7   "This will be something new, and new things are fun," Eddie told her. He knew his sister would have to be coaxed into trying the new drink.

8   "I don't like to eat new things," Marcy grumbled as she left the kitchen. If Eddie was determined to do this, she was not going to stay there and watch him!

9   When Marcy returned to the kitchen later, Eddie had finished making the juice. It was very green. She watched as he lifted a glass full of juice to his mouth and gulped some down. She held her breath.

10   "How does it taste?" she wanted to know.

11   "Magnificent!" Eddie grinned. "I'd even call it a <u>masterpiece</u>! I am a juice artist!" He extended the glass in her direction. He knew she would give in and drink the juice.

12   Marcy did not like the look of it, but now she was curious. She poured a little bit of the green liquid into a small glass and took a tiny sip. The taste of the juice surprised her. She thought it tasted a little like apple juice and a little like grape juice.

13   "This is good," she admitted. "What did you put in it to make it green and give it this flavor?"

14   "I have a secret ingredient," Eddie smiled.

15   "What is it?" Marcy asked.

16   "If I told you, it wouldn't be secret anymore, would it?"

GO ON

Page 3

1 What makes Eddie's juice different from most other juices?

- (A) Its size
- (B) Its taste
- (C) Its color
- (D) Its temperature

2 How is Marcy different from Eddie?

- (A) She does not like to try new things.
- (B) She likes to have adventures and take risks.
- (C) She thinks green is a good color for juice.
- (D) She never follows directions to make food.

3 Where did Eddie get the idea for green juice?

- (A) His dad suggested it.
- (B) He found it in a magazine.
- (C) Marcy dared him to do it.
- (D) He saw it on television.

4 In paragraph 2, what does the phrase "lost your marbles" mean?

- (A) Lost a favorite toy
- (B) Made a mistake
- (C) Forgotten your manners
- (D) Gone crazy

GO ON

5 In paragraph 3, the word <u>recipes</u> means —

   Ⓐ sets of directions

   Ⓑ food labels

   Ⓒ times for cooking

   Ⓓ kitchen tools

6 What does the word <u>masterpiece</u> mean in paragraph 11?

   Ⓐ An old story

   Ⓑ A great work

   Ⓒ An unusual food

   Ⓓ A glass of juice

7 How are Marcy's and Eddie's feelings about the green juice different, and how are they alike? Explain your answer and support it with details from the story.

_____

_____

_____

_____

_____

_____

_____

© Macmillan/McGraw-Hill

GO ON ➡

Read the introduction and the passage that follows. Then read each question and fill in the correct answer.

Grace wrote this story about holidays. She wants you to review her paper. As you read, think about the corrections and improvements that Grace should make. Then answer the questions that follow.

Holiday Baking

(1) My favorite month of the year is Desember. (2) I like winter, and I love the holidays. (3) Just before the holidays my family starts baking. (4) We enjoy baking cookies, cakes, and special holiday breads. (5) We also enjoy being together at the kitchen.

(6) Making the same recipes every year can bring back happy memories of past holidays. (7) Of course it is also fun to try new kinds of breads and cookies. (8) Who knows, maybe some of them will become your new family favorites!

GO ON ▶

8 What change, if any, should be made in sentence 1?

    A Change *month* to **months**

    B Change *is* to **are**

    C Change *Desember* to **December**

    D Make no change

9 What change, if any, should be made in sentence 2?

    A Change *like* to **likes**

    B Change *winter* to **wintter**

    C Change *holidays* to **holidayes**

    D Make no change

10 What change, if any, should be made in sentence 3?

    A Change *before* to **beside**

    B Insert a comma after *holidays*

    C Change *baking* to **baked**

    D Make no change

11 What change, if any, should be made in sentence 5?

    A Change *We* to **Us**

    B Change *being* to **be**

    C Change *at* to **in**

    D Make no change

12 What change, if any, should be made in sentence 7?

    A Insert a comma after *course*

    B Change *is* to **be**

    C Change *try* to **trying**

    D Make no change

STOP

Grade 3 • Unit 6 • Week 4
Student Evaluation Chart

Tested Skills	Number Correct	Percent Correct
Reading Comprehension: *Compare and Contrast (fiction), 1, 2; Make Inferences, 3*	/3	%
Short Answer: *Compare and Contrast (fiction), 7*	/3	%
Vocabulary Strategies: *Dictionary: Idiom, 4; Context Clues, 5, 6*	/3	%
Grammar, Mechanics, and Usage: *Commas after Introductory Words, 10, 12; Prepositions and Prepositional Phrases, 11*	/3	%
Spelling: *r-Controlled Vowel Syllables, 8, 9*	/2	%
Total Weekly Test Score	/14	%

Student Name _____

Date _____

Weekly Assessment

TESTED SKILLS AND STRATEGIES

- **Reading Comprehension**
- **Vocabulary Strategies**
- **Grammar, Mechanics, and Usage**
- **Spelling**

Mc Graw Hill **Macmillan/McGraw-Hill**

DIRECTIONS

Read "A Riddle for Jeremy." Then read each question. Decide which is the best answer to each question. Mark the space for the answer you have chosen. Write your answer to question 7.

A Riddle for Jeremy

1   Jeremy always tried to be the best, no matter what he was doing. He just had to win. He had to be first place in the spelling bee. He even had to shoot the most baskets in gym. But Jeremy's biggest wish was to do better than his classmate, Chris Jones. But Chris also liked to win. Sometimes, he even beat Jeremy. But Jeremy would never get <u>discouraged</u>. He would just try harder next time.

2   One day, the teacher announced, "We are going to hold a race to raise money for a new computer. People will give money for you to run. You should ask some people to help you. I hope many of you can sign up for this event." Jeremy was not the swiftest runner, but the thought of winning made him sign up right away.

© Macmillan/McGraw-Hill

GO ON ▶

Page 2

3   As Jeremy walked home from school, he saw Chris asking neighbors and friends to support him for the race. Chris gave out fliers telling all about the school computer. But Jeremy didn't want to waste his time. He just wanted to win.

4   At dinner, Jeremy asked his father to give money in his name. He could tell from his father's raised eyebrow that his answer was no. "You are running for the wrong reason," his father said. "You should be running to help your school. Winning is not always a good reason for doing something."

5   "So?" said Jeremy.

6   "Here is a riddle," replied his father. "If you run the race with no donations, but pass the person in first place, who would be the winner?"

7   "I would be the winner," said Jeremy proudly. He was sure he had the right answer.

8   His father just shook his head.

9   On the day of the race, it was boiling hot. Sand blew up from the track as the runners prepared to depart. The whistle blew and the race began.

10   Jeremy ran as fast as he could, but sand got in his eyes. People pushed him off the track. Jeremy tried to increase his speed, but even though he went faster, the finish line was still far away. He gasped for breath. His legs ached. Wearily, he pushed on. Near the end of the race, he suddenly sped up and passed Chris, who was in first place. Jeremy was the first one to cross the finish line, but he was not the winner.

11   Do you know why?

GO ON ▶

1 Look at the chart below.

Character	Plot
Jeremy always tried to be the best.	

Which of these belongs in the empty box?

A Jeremy needed a new computer.

B Jeremy asked his father for money.

C Jeremy wanted to win the race.

D Jeremy got pushed off the track.

---

2 What did Jeremy and his father disagree about?

A Whether Jeremy is a fast runner

B Jeremy's reason for running the race

C Whether the school needed a computer

D How much money he would get for the race

3 Where does the last part of the story take place?

A At Jeremy's house

B In the school gym

C In a classroom

D On a race track

4 In paragraph 1, the word discouraged means —

A made to feel hopeless

B prepared to run

C confident about his skill

D able to win

GO ON

5 Which meaning from the dictionary fits the word <u>depart</u> in paragraph 9?

- Ⓐ To run fast
- Ⓑ To leave a place
- Ⓒ To warm up
- Ⓓ To follow closely

6 Which meaning from the dictionary fits the word <u>increase</u> in paragraph 10?

- Ⓐ A long race
- Ⓑ To finish first
- Ⓒ A sudden rise
- Ⓓ To make greater

7 What lesson does Jeremy's father want him to learn when he asks Jeremy the riddle? Explain your answer and support it with details from the story.

_____

_____

_____

_____

_____

_____

_____

GO ON ➡

DIRECTIONS

Read the introduction and the passage that follows. Then read each question and fill in the correct answer.

Grace wrote this story about a swim meet. She wants you to review her paper. As you read, think about the corrections and improvements that Grace should make. Then answer the questions that follow.

Swim Meet

(1) It is the day of the swim meet. (2) There will be swimming diving, and relay races. (3) At one end of the pool the crowd cheers as a swimmer crosses the finish line. (4) The crowd at the other end is silent as a girl prepares to dive. (5) She walks carefuly to the end of the board and stands at the edge for a moment. (6) She looks confident. (7) She stares calmly into the pool. (8) Suddenly, she dives in. (9) Her body slices through the water like a knife. (10) She makes it look so easy and painles. (11) Everyone claps for her.

GO ON

8 What change, if any, should be made in sentence 2?

- **A** Change *will be* to **being**
- **B** Insert a comma after *swimming*
- **C** Change *diving* to **divving**
- **D** Make no change

9 What change, if any, should be made in sentence 3?

- **A** Insert a comma after *pool*
- **B** Change *swimmer* to **swimer**
- **C** Change *crosses* to **cross**
- **D** Make no change

10 What change, if any, should be made in sentence 5?

- **A** Change *walks* to **walk**
- **B** Change *carefuly* to **carefully**
- **C** Change *at* to **in**
- **D** Make no change

11 What is the **BEST** way to revise sentences 6 and 7?

- **A** She looks confident unless she stares calmly into the pool.
- **B** She looks with confidence when she stares calm into the pool.
- **C** She looks confidently and stares with calmness into the pool.
- **D** She looks confident as she stares calmly into the pool.

12 What change, if any, should be made in sentence 10?

- **A** Change *She* to **Her**
- **B** Change *makes* to **make**
- **C** Change *painles* to **painless**
- **D** Make no change

STOP

Grade 3 • Unit 6 • Week 5
Student Evaluation Chart

Tested Skills	Number Correct	Percent Correct
Reading Comprehension: *Character, Setting, Plot,* 1, 2, 3	/3	%
Short Answer: *Character, Setting, Plot,* 7	/3	%
Vocabulary Strategies: *Context Clues,* 4; *Dictionary: Unfamiliar Words,* 5, 6	/3	%
Grammar, Mechanics, and Usage: *Commas,* 8, 9; *Sentence Combining with Adjectives and Adverbs,* 11	/3	%
Spelling: *Words with Suffixes (-ful, -less, -ly, -able),* 10, 12	/2	%
Total Weekly Test Score	**/14**	**%**

Notes

Notes

Notes

Notes

Notes

Notes

Notes

Notes

Notes

Notes

Notes

Notes